INTERSCIENCE MONOGRAPHS ON CHEMISTRY

Interscience Monographs on Chemistry

INORGANIC CHEMISTRY SECTION

Edited by F. Albert Cotton and G. Wilkinson

GOODENOUGH   Magnetism and the Chemical Bond

COLTON   The Chemistry of Rhenium and Technetium

Other volumes to follow

The Chemistry of
RHENIUM
and
TECHNETIUM

R. COLTON

University of Melbourne

1965
INTERSCIENCE PUBLISHERS
a division of John Wiley & Sons Ltd.
London· NewYork · Sydney

Printed in Great Britain by Page Bros. (Norwich) Ltd.

Preface

It is now almost forty years since rhenium was discovered and nearly thirty years since technetium was identified. Progress in rhenium chemistry was steady but not spectacular before the war, but since about 1950 the amount of published research on rhenium has increased yearly at a very rapid rate. Technetium presents a different picture. Prior to the war the only experiments possible were on tracer amounts of the element produced by cyclotron irradiations of molybdenum. Nothing was heard of technetium during the war although it was subsequently made clear that it had been identified as a fission product of uranium. The amounts of technetium available for research were still very small after the war, indeed it was not until 1952 that the first gramme of the element was isolated. Mainly as a result of painstaking work at the Oak Ridge National Laboratory technetium is now fairly readily available to universities and research institutions. So far the amount of work, and type of work, attempted with technetium has been governed by its scarcity, but this is no longer so important and the time is ripe for a rapid expansion of technetium chemistry.

With this situation in mind it seemed to be an ideal time to produce this book on rhenium and technetium. The broad features of rhenium chemistry are now well established but there are still very many gaps and details to be filled. The little we know of technetium suggests, as we would expect, that it resembles rhenium quite closely so that it is appropriate to deal with the two elements together.

I have quite deliberately chosen to deal with rhenium first in each chapter since so much more is known of its behaviour than that of technetium that this arrangement makes comparisons easier. I have also deliberately omitted any discussion of alloys.

The major part of the library work involved in the preparation of this book was done whilst I was employed at the Atomic Energy Research Establishment, Harwell. I am greatly indebted to the United Kingdom Atomic Energy Authority for these library facilities and also laboratory facilities for experimental work with technetium and rhenium in the period 1960–63.

My sincere thanks are also due to Professor Geoffrey Wilkinson, Imperial College, London, who originally suggested that this book be written and who has been a source of valuable encouragement to me. Professor R. L. Martin and Dr. T. A. O'Donnell of this Department read the manuscript and made many constructive criticisms. To them, and to Mrs. J. A. Vike who typed the manuscript, I am very grateful.

R. COLTON

University of Melbourne,
Victoria, Australia.

Contents

1

Isolation of the Elements and their General Properties

The Occurrence and Isolation of Rhenium

There are no rhenium minerals. Rhenium is one of the rarest of the non-radioactive elements, a fact which no doubt delayed its discovery until 1925. The credit for the discovery of element 75 is usually given to Noddack, Tacke and Berg[1] although other claims were made at about the same time.[2, 3] The original claim has been criticized because it was said that the element was detected in platinum ores. Subsequently Noddack and coworkers used molybdenum sulphide ores as their primary source of the metal and since that time rhenium has not been isolated from platinum ores.

Early laboratory separations of rhenium from molybdenum ores involved dissolution of the mineral in concentrated nitric acid and subsequent separation of the rhenium by precipitation of rhenium hepta-sulphide,[4] by separation of potassium perrhenate[5] or by distillation of rhenium heptaoxide from acid solutions.[6]

Rhenium is recovered commercially as a by-product of the treatment of molybdenum ores and also copper ores.[7] In each case the ores are roasted in air; rhenium heptaoxide is formed and volatilizes out of the furnace. It may be recovered either from the stack or flue dusts or removed from the waste gases using a dry cyclone and a wet scrubber.[8] The recovered heptaoxide is usually dissolved in water and the rhenium finally recovered by crystallization of potassium perrhenate. Potassium perrhenate has very convenient solubility properties which make it a good form in which to isolate rhenium. A book describing Russian practice in recovering rhenium has recently been published.[9]

The metal used to be prepared by reduction of potassium perrhenate by hydrogen. It is difficult to obtain complete reduction and some potassium

1

is always retained even after repeated leachings with dilute acids. The presence of potassium in the rhenium metal is not usually important but recent use of rhenium filaments in mass spectrometers has made it necessary to prepare rhenium free from potassium. This is usually done by reducing ammonium perrhenate instead of the potassium salt.

On the laboratory scale pure metallic rhenium has been prepared by the chlorination of crude rhenium to give first the pentachloride. This was then hydrolysed in water to give rhenium dioxide which was then reduced to the metal by hydrogen.[10] A different process involved the thermal decomposition of ammonium hexaiodorhenate (IV) in vacuum at 700°.[11]

The Natural Occurrence of Technetium

There have been many claims to the isolation of element 43 from natural sources. Perhaps the most famous claim is that of Noddack and coworkers[1] who thought they had discovered the element, which they called masurium, at the same time as they isolated rhenium. The history of earlier claims to the discovery of element 43 has been excellently reviewed by Kenna.[12]

The credit for the discovery of element 43 is given to Perrier and Segré who identified some radiations from a molybdenum plate which had been bombarded with deuterons as being due to radioactive isotopes of the missing element.[13, 14] They later[15] suggested the name technetium, from a Greek word meaning artificial, since it was the first previously unknown element to be prepared artificially. This name has been officially accepted by the International Union of Pure and Applied Chemistry.[16]

Many isotopes of technetium have been prepared since 1937. One of the most interesting was ^{98}Tc which was known to be long-lived although the actual half-life was unknown. It was known however that the other isotopes of technetium all had half-lives too short for any primordial technetium to still exist in the earth's crust. Recent searches for technetium in nature have therefore been directed towards finding ^{98}Tc. Probably the most sensitive method of detecting ^{98}Tc is neutron activation analysis making use of the 6 hour half-life of the internal transition from ^{99m}Tc to ^{99g}Tc,

$$^{98}\text{Tc} \, (n, \gamma)^{99m}\text{Tc} \xrightarrow[\text{6.0 h}]{\text{i.t.}} {}^{99g}\text{Tc}$$

and in fact all investigators who searched for ^{98}Tc in nature used this procedure.

Herr[17] looked for technetium in a number of minerals from Norway and South Africa which were rich in rhenium. The results however were inconclusive since the final precipitate after irradiation showed the presence of large amounts of rhenium indicating that the technetium–rhenium separation was not efficient.

Alperovitch and Miller[18] reported the presence of primordial technetium in columbite. The technetium was isolated by a series of precipitation and distillation techniques and finally purified by ion exchange methods. After irradiation the gamma radiation of ^{99m}Tc was identified for several samples.

Subsequent work by Anders, Sen Sarma and Kato[19] also appeared to indicate that technetium occurred naturally. The technetium was again isolated by precipitation, distillation and ion exchange procedures in a similar manner to the methods of Alperovitch and Miller. Some allowance was given to the possibility of the technetium being produced by nuclear reactions on molybdenum in the samples but even allowing for this possibility the results seemed to indicate that some technetium existed in th samples. Soon after these results were published Boyd and Larson[20] showed that the half-life of ^{98}Tc was of the order of 1×10^5 years, thus excluding the possibility of any primordial technetium still existing in the earth's crust. Moreover they made a careful re-examination of several minerals which had previously been said to contain traces of technetium with negative results. Although neutron activation analysis is the most sensitive method of detecting ^{98}Tc it is open to interferences from several sources. The sample must not contain any molybdenum because of reactions such as

$$^{98}\text{Mo (n, } \gamma)^{99}\text{Mo} \xrightarrow{\;67\,\text{h}\;} {}^{99m}\text{Tc} \xrightarrow{\;6.0\,\text{h}\;} {}^{99g}\text{Tc}$$

In addition care must be taken that the samples are not contaminated by ^{99g}Tc, as was observed by Boyd and Larson[20] for one of their samples. ^{99g}Tc undergoes reaction with neutrons of energy greater than 140 Kev by inelastic collision to give the metastable isomer ^{99m}Tc

$$^{99g}\text{Tc (n, n')}^{99m}\text{Tc} \xrightarrow{\;6.0\,\text{h}\;} {}^{99g}\text{Tc}$$

with the subsequent decay of ^{99m}Tc with its characteristic half-life. It appears that considerations of this type explain the previous observations of technetium in minerals.

Isotope dilution analysis using a mass spectrometer is not so sensitive as neutron activation analysis but it is not open to the same interferences as the latter method. Boyd and Larson used isotope dilution analysis and failed to find any trace of technetium in minerals. It now seems clear that no primordial technetium exists in the earth's crust.

The most recent attempts to isolate technetium from natural sources have been directed towards technetium produced by spontaneous fission of uranium isotopes, especially ^{238}U. The equilibrium amounts of technetium produced in uranium ores would be given by the equation[12]

$$Y_{99}N^{238}\lambda_{238f} = N^{99}\lambda_{99}$$

where N^{238} and N^{99} are the number of atoms of ^{238}U and ^{99}Tc respectively; λ_{238f} and λ_{99} are the spontaneous fission decay constants of ^{238}U and of ^{99}Tc respectively, and Y_{99} is the fission yield of ^{99}Tc which is known to be approximately 6%. Substituting numerical values shows that there should be about 2.5×10^{-10} g of technetium (10.5 disintegrations per minute) per kilogramme of pitchblende (50% uranium).[12]

There is also a contribution to the total technetium content of the uranium ores from the slow neutron-induced fission of ^{235}U, but this has been shown[21] to produce only approximately 25% of the amount of technetium produced by spontaneous fission of ^{238}U.

The first isolation and identification of naturally occurring technetium was recently reported by Kenna and Kuroda.[22] After dissolution of the pitchblende in nitric acid a series of precipitations, solvent extractions and ion exchange procedures produced a technetium fraction. A small amount of copper was added as a carrier in the final sulphide precipitation before assaying the technetium directly by counting techniques. About 1 mμg of technetium was isolated from 5.3 kg of pitchblende.

Technetium has been detected in certain stars but a claim[23] that technetium lines were present in the spectrum of the sun was erroneous.[24] Merrill has identified lines due to Tc^I in S-type stars[25] and more recently in N-type stars.[26] The discovery of technetium in stars has greatly influenced recent theories of stellar evolution and element synthesis which must explain its presence in these stars.[27]

The Isolation of Artificial Technetium

The first weighable amount of technetium was produced by the neutron irradiation of 5.7 kg of molybdenum metal powder in a nuclear reactor.[28] The nuclear reaction involved in the synthesis is

$$^{98}Mo\ (n,\ \gamma)\ ^{99}Mo\ \xrightarrow[\beta^-]{67\ h}\ ^{99m}Tc\ \xrightarrow{6.0\ h}\ ^{99g}Tc$$

The technetium was readily separated from the bulk of the molybdenum by dissolving the metal in concentrated sulphuric acid and distilling the volatile technetium heptaoxide from the solution. Using platinum sulphide as a carrier the technetium was precipitated from the distillate as the heptasulphide. The sulphide was then dissolved in hydrogen peroxide and the sequence of distillation and sulphide precipitation repeated several times. This separation scheme not only concentrated the technetium formed by the nuclear reaction but also the small amounts of rhenium which were present as an impurity in the molybdenum. The final separation from rhenium was accomplished by repeating the sulphide separation in hydrochloric acid more concentrated than 8 м. Under these conditions only rhenium heptasulphide precipitated leaving the technetium in solution.

Irradiation of molybdenum is unsuitable for the production of large amounts of technetium and accordingly attention was soon turned to the recovery of technetium from fission products.

The fission of uranium in a nuclear reactor gives rise to many fission products but about 6% of the total yield is technetium. With the ever increasing number of nuclear reactors coming into operation this represents a very considerable production of technetium. During the recycling of the irradiated fuel through the separation plant the technetium follows the majority of the other fission products into the waste solutions. After storage for several years the level of radioactivity in these solutions is considerably reduced because of the decay of the short-lived fission products and it is then possible to extract the longer-lived fission products, including technetium.

Parker, Reed and Ruch[29] isolated milligramme amounts of fission product technetium from several kilogrammes of uranium which had been irradiated in a nuclear reactor. The fuel elements were dissolved in 37% hydrochloric acid and the resulting slurry of uranium tetrachloride was oxidized to uranyl chloride with bromine water. The technetium was separated by sulphide precipitation using platinum sulphide as a carrier and finally purified by a cycle of distillations of the oxide from sulphuric acid solution and sulphide precipitations.

The first gramme of technetium was isolated from fission product waste solutions by precipitating tetraphenylarsonium pertechnetate using tetraphenylarsonium perchlorate as a carrier.[30] The mixed salts were dissolved in concentrated sulphuric acid and the solution electrolysed between platinum electrodes. A black deposit, which was probably technetium dioxide, was obtained. This was dissolved in concentrated sulphuric acid and technetium heptaoxide was then distilled and the element finally isolated as its sulphide. The electrolysis procedure had the disadvantage that the expensive tetraphenylarsonium cation was destroyed. In a modification of the procedure the mixed precipitate of tetraphenylarsonium pertechnetate and perchlorate was dissolved in alcohol and passed through an ion exchange column in the cloride form. The pertechnetate and perchlorate ions were strongly absorbed and tetraphenylarsonium chloride was recovered from the eluent. The technetium was then eluted quantitatively from the resin with 2 M sodium hydroxide solution.

Technetium is now isolated from fission product wastes by solvent extraction and ion exchange procedures and production amounts to several kilogrammes per year.[31]

Nuclear Properties

Table 1-1. Isotopes of rhenium

Isotope	Half-life and mode of decay	Preparation	Ref.
^{177}Re	17 min $\beta+$	^{182}W (120 Mev p, 6n)^{177}Re	36
^{178}Re	18 min $\beta+$	^{182}W (120 Mev p, 5n)^{178}Re	36
^{180}Re	2.4 min $\beta+$	^{182}W (20 Mev p, 3n)^{180}Re	37
^{183}Re	70 d K capture	^{181}Ta (40 Mev α, 2n)^{183}Re	38
^{184}Re	50 d	^{181}Ta (28 Mev α, n)^{184}Re	39
^{185}Re	Stable, naturally occurring		
^{186}Re	3.8 d $\beta-$	^{183}Re (n, γ)^{186}Re	40
^{187}Re	about 5×10^{10} y $\beta-$ naturally occurring		41
^{188}Re	17 h $\beta-$	^{187}Re (n, γ)^{188}Re	40
^{189}Re	9.8 min $\beta-$	^{187}Re (2n, γ)^{189}Re	42

Table 1-2. Isotopes of technetium

Isotope	Half-life and mode of decay	Preparation	Ref.
^{93}Tc	^{93m}Tc 43.5 min i.t. ^{93g}Tc 2.8 h K	^{92}Mo (p, γ)^{93}Tc ^{92}Mo (α, n)^{93}Tc	43, 44, 45
^{94}Tc	52.2 min $\beta+ K$	^{94}Mo (d, 2n)^{94}Tc ^{94}Mo (p, n)^{94}Tc	44, 46, 47
^{95}Tc	^{95m}Tc 60 d K ^{95g}Tc 20 h K	^{95}Mo (p, n)^{95}Tc ^{92}Mo (α, p)^{95}Tc	47, 48
^{96}Tc	^{96m}Tc 51.5 min i.t. ^{96g}Tc 4.3 d K	^{95}Mo (p, γ)^{96} ^{93}Nb (α, n)^{96}Tc	47, 48
^{97}Tc	^{97m}Tc 90 d i.t. ^{97}Tc 2.6×10^6 y K	^{96}Ru (n, γ)^{97}Ru $\rightarrow$ ^{97}Tc ^{97}Mo (α, 2n)^{97}Tc	48, 49
^{98}Tc	2×10^6 y ?	^{98}Mo (p, n)^{98}Tc	50, 51
^{99}Tc	^{99m}Tc 5.9 h ^{99g}Tc 2.12×10^5 y $\beta-$	^{98}Mo (p, n)^{99}Mo $\rightarrow$ ^{99}Tc fission of U (6.2%)	52–56
^{100}Tc	15.8 sec ?	^{100}Mo (p, n)^{100}Tc ^{99}Tc (n, γ)^{100}Tc	57, 58
^{101}Tc	15 min $\beta-$	^{100}Mo (d, n)^{101}Tc	59

$K = K$ electron capture   i.t. = internal transition
m = metastable state   g = ground state

Rhenium occurs naturally with two isotopes, [185]Re and [187]Re, in such proportions that the physically determined atomic weight is 186.22.[32-34] The chemically determined atomic weight is 186.31.[35] Many radioactive isotopes of rhenium have been prepared and some of the more important ones are listed in Table 1-1.

Perrier and Segré identified the isotopes [95]Tc and [97]Tc when they discovered technetium. Since that time many other isotopes have been prepared and some of the more important ones are listed in Table 1-2.

Properties of the Metals

Rhenium metal is usually produced as a dark grey or black powder which may be converted to wire or sheet by powder metallurgical techniques. It is produced by hydrogen reduction of potassium perrhenate, ammonium perrhenate or sometimes rhenium sulphides. It is a fairly reactive metal, dissolving in oxidizing acids to give perrhenic acid, but it is not dissolved by hydrochloric acid. The powder is readily oxidized when heated in air; all of the halogens with the exception of iodine combine directly with the metal. The metal dissolves in hydrogen peroxide although in the author's experience different batches of powder vary considerably in their ease of dissolution presumably because of particle size effects.

Rhenium has a close packed hexagonal lattice similar to that of osmium. The dimensions of the unit cell have been determined several times[60-63] with slightly varying results but the mean value is $a = 2.760$ Å and $c = 4.458$ Å. The atomic radius is 1.37 Å which lies between those of tungsten and osmium.

The latest value for the melting point of rhenium is $3180 \pm 20°$.[63, 64] The estimated boiling point is $5630°$.[65]

The magnetic properties of rhenium metal have been investigated several times but there is some variation in the recorded susceptibilities. Perakis and Capatos[66] obtained a susceptibility of 0.366×10^{-6} e.m.u. Asmussen and Soling[67] studied two samples both of which gave virtually temperature-independent paramagnetism although the values of the susceptibilities differed from each other. The values obtained for the two samples were

$$\text{Re (1) } \chi_g \times 10^6 = 0.280 + 0.0000075\,T$$
$$\text{Re (2) } \chi_g \times 10^6 = 0.310 + 0.000017\,T$$

The low temperature heat capacity of metallic rhenium has been measured between 20–300°κ by adiabatic calorimetry, and thermodynamic functions of rhenium have been calculated.[68]

B

Colloidal rhenium is formed by the reduction of potassium hexachloro-rhenate (IV) with hydrazine and formaldehyde in the presence of gum arabic.[69] The colloid was said to be stable for months. It absorbed hydrogen and catalysed the formation of ammonia from its elements.

Many papers have been published on the electroplating of rhenium from solutions, but all investigators have agreed that sulphuric acid solutions give the best coatings of rhenium. The results of several investigations are given in Table 1-3. In some cases[71, 72] it is stated that the films deposited

Table 1-3. Electroplating of rhenium from sulphuric acid solutions

Rhenium compound	Concentration (g/l)	Acidity of H_2SO_4 solution	Current density (A/dm²)	Temp.	Ref.
KReO₄	10–25	pH 0.8–1.0	10–16	25–45°	70
KReO₄	11	pH 0.9	10–14	25–45°	71, 72
HReO₄	20	pH 0.7–1.2	10–14	25–30°	73
KReO₄	10	pH 0.9–1.0	15	85–90°	74
KReO₄	10–12	pH 0.8–1.0	50	—	75

are not durable. Better deposits are obtained if only a thin film of rhenium is deposited followed by annealing at high temperature. Further deposits of rhenium are then added in a similar manner and in this way a heavy deposit may be obtained which has good chemical and mechanical stability.

Rhenium is fabricated using powder techniques and cold working.[76] Bars of compressed and sintered rhenium powder are converted to sheet and wire by mild cold working with intermediate annealing at high temperatures. Attempts at hot working produced cracks in the metal presumably due to oxide formation.

Technetium metal has been obtained by the hydrogen reduction of the heptasulphide[77] at 1100° and by the hydrogen reduction of ammonium pertechnetate.[78] In the latter method it is usual to reduce the ammonium pertechnetate to technetium dioxide at about 200° followed by reduction to the metal at about 500–600°. The reduction of ammonium pertechnetate gives very pure technetium metal. A more recent method of preparation of technetium metal is to heat ammonium hexachlorotechnate (IV), $(NH_4)_2TcCl_6$, in nitrogen to red heat.[79] Technetium has been electroplated from solution by electrolysis of a solution of ammonium pertechnetate in 1 M sulphuric acid. The original report[80] suggested that it was necessary to have a trace of fluoride ion in the solution to obtain a bright deposit of technetium metal, but the latest investigation[79] of the system showed that a good deposit could be obtained in the absence of fluoride ion.

Parker[81] found that technetium melted at $2140 \pm 20°$ and a later determination[82] fixed the melting point at $2250 \pm 50°$. The metal crystallizes in a close-packed hexagonal arrangement isomorphous with that of rhenium.[83] The chemical properties of technetium are quite similar to those of rhenium. It dissolves in oxidizing acids and contrary to early reports[78] it does dissolve in hydrogen peroxide.[84] No doubt its reactivity towards this reagent varies quite considerably with particle size as noted for rhenium.

References

1. W. NODDACK, I. TACKE and O. BERG, *Naturwissenschaften* **13**, 567 (1925).
2. J. G. F. DRUCE, *Chem. News* **131**, 273 (1925).
3. V. DOLEJSEK and J. HEYROVSKY, *Nature* **116**, 782 (1925).
4. I. and W. NODDACK, *Z. Physik. Chem.* **125**, 264 (1927).
5. W. FEIT, *Angew. Chem.* **46**, 216 (1933).
6. G. T. MORGAN, *J. Chem. Soc.* 567 (1935).
7. T. A. SATPAEVA, S. K. KALININ and E. E. FAIN, *Vestn. Akad. Nauk Kaz. SSR* **15**, 52 (1959).
8. V. P. SAORAEV and E. A. SAMKOV, *Tsvetn. Metal.* **33**, 53 (1960).
9. A. A. LEBEDEV, *The Chemistry of Rhenium*, Butterworth, London (1962).
10. D. M. ROSENBAUM, R. J. RUNCH and I. E. CAMPBELL, *J. Electrochem. Soc.* **103**, 518 (1956).
11. A. A. WOOLF, *J. Inorg. Nucl. Chem.* **7**, 291 (1958).
12. B. T. KENNA, *J. Chem. Educ.* **39**, 436 (1962).
13. C. PERRIER and E. SEGRÉ, *J. Chem. Phys.* **5**, 712 (1937).
14. C. PERRIER and E. SEGRÉ, *J. Chem. Phys.* **7**, 155 (1939).
15. C. PERRIER and E. SEGRÉ, *Nature* **159**, 24 (1947).
16. Committee on New Elements, *I.U.P.A.C. Chem. Eng. News* **27**, 2996 (1946).
17. W. HERR, *Naturforsch. A*, **9**, 907 (1954).
18. E. ALPEROVITCH and J. MILLER, *Nature* **176**, 299 (1955).
19. E. ANDERS, R. SEN SARMA and P. KATO, *J. Phys. Chem.* **24**, 622 (1956).
20. G. E. BOYD and Q. V. LARSON, *J. Phys. Chem.* **60**, 707 (1956).
21. B. T. KENNA and P. K. KURODA, *J. Inorg. Nucl. Chem.* **16**, 1 (1960).
22. B. T. KENNA and P. K. KURODA, *J. Inorg. Nucl. Chem.* **23**, 142 (1961).
23. C. MOORE, *Science* **114**, 59 (1951).
24. J. GREENSTEIN and C. DE JAGER, *Bull. Astron. Inst. Neth.* **19**, 13 (1957).
25. P. W. MERRILL, *Astrophys. J.* **116**, 21 (1952).
26. P. W. MERRILL, *Publ. Astron. Soc. Pacific* **68**, 70 (1956).
27. A. W. CAMERON, *Astrophys. J.* **121**, 144 (1955).
28. G. E. BOYD, Q. V. LARSON and E. E. MOTTA, *Unclassified Document, A.E.C.D.* 2151 (1948).
29. G. W. PARKER, J. REED and J. RUCH, *Unclassified Document, A.E.C.D.* 2043 (1948).
30. J. W. COBBLE, C. M. NELSON, G. W. PARKER, W. T. SMITH, JNR. and G. E. BOYD, *J. Am. Chem. Soc.* **74**, 1852 (1952).
31. G. E. BOYD, *J. Chem. Educ.* **36**, 3 (1959).
32. F. ASTON, *Proc. Roy. Soc. (London) A*, **132**, 487 (1931).

33. J. R. WHITE and A. E. CAMERON, *Phys. Rev.* **74**, 991 (1948).
34. L. FRIEDMAN, A. P. IRSA and G. WILKINSON, *J. Am. Chem. Soc.* **77**, 3689 (1955).
35. O. HONIGSCHMIDT and R. SACHTLEBEN, *Z. Anorg. Allgem. Chem.* **191**, 309 (1930).
36. B. C. HALDAR and E. O. WIIG, *Phys. Rev.* **105**, 1285 (1957).
37. V. K. FISCHER, *Phys. Rev.* **99**, 764 (1955).
38. D. STROMINGEN, *Phys. Rev.* **97**, 1007 (1955).
39. S. THULIN, J. O. RASMUSSEN, C. J. GALLAGHER, JNR., W. G. SMITH and J. M. HOLLANDER, *Phys. Rev.* **104**, 471 (1956).
40. M. W. JOHNS, C. C. MCMULLEN, I. R. WILLIAMS and S. V. NABLO, *Phys. Rev.* **91**, 418 (1953).
41. H. HINTENBERGER, W. HERR and H. VOSHAGE, *Phys. Rev.* **95**, 1691 (1954).
42. R. R. SMITH, *J. Inorg. Nucl. Chem.* **3**, 157 (1956).
43. H. EASTERDAY and H. MEDICUS, *Phys. Rev.* **89**, 752 (1953).
44. E. E. MOTTA and G. E. BOYD, *Phys. Rev.* **74**, 220 (1948).
45. C. LEVI and L. PAPINEAU, *Compt. rend.* **239**, 2313 (1954).
46. O. HUBER, P. MARMIER, H. MEDICUS, P. PRIESWERK and R. STEFFEN, *Phys. Rev.* **73**, 1208 (1948).
47. H. MEDICUS, P. PRIESWERK and W. SCHERRER, *Helv. Phys. Acta* **23**, 299 (1950).
48. E. E. MOTTA and G. E. BOYD, *Phys. Rev.* **74**, 344 (1948).
49. G. E. BOYD, *Phys. Rev.* **95**, 113 (1954).
50. G. E. BOYD, J. R. SITES, Q. V. LARSON and C. R. BALDOCK, *Phys. Rev.* **99**, 1030 (1955).
51. S. KATCOFF, *Phys. Rev.* **99**, 1618 (1955).
52. G. T. SEABORG and E. SEGRÉ, *Phys. Rev.* **55**, 808 (1939).
53. D. C. LINCOLN and R. P. SULLIVAN, *Natl. Nucl. Energy Ser.* Div. IV **9**, 228 (1951).
54. E. E. MOTTA, G. E. BOYD and Q. V. LARSON, *Phys. Rev.* **72**, 1270 (1947).
55. R. P. SULLIVAN, *Natl. Nucl. Energy Ser.* Div. IV **9**, 783 (1951).
56. E. SEGRÉ and C. S. WU, *Phys. Rev.* **57**, 552 (1940).
57. R. A. HOUSE, R. L. COLLIGAN, D. N. KUNDA and M. L. POOL, *Phys. Rev.* **86**, 654 (1952).
58. G. E. BOYD, Q. V. LARSON and G. W. PARKER, *Phys. Rev.* **86**, 1051 (1952).
59. G. E. BOYD and B. H. KETELLE, *Phys. Rev.* **83**, 216 (1951).
60. V. M. GOLDSCHMIDT, *Naturwissenschaften* **17**, 134 (1929).
61. C. AGTE, H. ALTHERTUM, K. BECKER, G. HEYNE and K. MOERS, *Naturwissenschaften* **19**, 108 (1931).
62. W. STENZEL and J. WEERTS, *Z. Krist.* **84**, 20 (1933).
63. C. T. SIMS, C. M. CRAIGHEAD and R. I. JAFFEE, *J. Metals* **7**, *A.I.M.E. Trans.* **203**, 168 (1955).
64. C. T. SIMS and R. I. JAFFEE, *J. Metals* **7**, *A.I.M.E. Trans.* **203**, 913 (1956).
65. E. M. SHERWOOD, D. M. ROSENBAUM, J. M. BLOCHER and I. E. CAMPBELL, *J. Electrochem. Soc.* **102**, 650 (1955).
66. N. PERAKIS and L. CAPATOS, *Compt. Rend.* **196**, 611 (1933).
67. R. W. ASMUSSEN and H. SOLING, *Acta Chem. Scand.* **8**, 563 (1954).
68. W. T. SMITH, JNR., G. D. OLIVER and J. W. COBBLE, *J. Am. Chem. Soc.* **75**, 5785 (1953).
69. C. ZENGHELIS and K. STATHIS, *Compt. Rend.* **209**, 797 (1939).

70. R. Levi, *U.S. Pat.* 2,616,840.
71. Phillips Electrical Ltd., *Brit. Pat.* 661,153 (1951).
72. N. V. Phillips, *Dutch Pat.* 72,568 (1963).
73. G. Fink and P. Deren, *German Pat.* 626,322 (1936).
74. I. I. Grozdeva and A. I. Zhurin, *Tsvetn. Metal.* **188**, 212 (1957).
75. S. I. Sklyarenko, Z. M. Sominskaya, A. A. Nikitina and I. I. Lavrov, *Redkie Metally i Splavy, Tru. Pervogo Vses. Soveshch. po Splavam Redkikh Metal., Akad. Nauk SSSR, Inst. Met.* 111 (1957).
76. Batelle Development Corporation, *Brit. Pat.* 768,795 (1957).
77. S. Fried, *J. Am. Chem. Soc.* **70**, 442 (1948).
78. J. W. Cobble, C. M. Nelson, G. W. Parker and W. T. Smith, Jnr., *J. Am. Chem. Soc.* **74**, 1852 (1952).
79. J. D. Eakins and D. G. Humphries, *J. Inorg. Nucl. Chem.* **25**, 737 (1963).
80. E. E. Motta, Q. V. Larson and G. E. Boyd, *Unclassified Document Mon.* C-99 (1947).
81. G. W. Parker, *Unclassified Document*, O.R.N.L. 1260 (1952).
82. E. Anderson, R. A. Buckley, A. Hellawell and W. Hume-Rothery, *Nature* **188**, 48 (1960).
83. R. C. L. Mooney, *Acta Cryst.* **1**, 161 (1948).
84. R. Colton and R. D. Peacock, *Quart. Rev. (London)* **16**, 299 (1962).

2

Separation Procedures and Analysis

In this chapter separations concerned with the analytical behaviour of rhenium and technetium, rather than separations concerned with the actual isolation of the elements, will be discussed. Nevertheless mention will be made of many molybdenum–rhenium and technetium–rhenium separations which have been used to isolate the elements.

Analytical Separations of Rhenium and Technetium

Most of the early work with rhenium was directed towards isolating the element by distillation of the volatile heptaoxide from sulphuric acid solutions or by precipitation as a sulphide which could be readily converted to perrhenate for determination by nitron.

It was found that rhenium in any valency state could be precipitated as a sulphide.[1] Trivalent rhenium precipitated slowly from hydrochloric acid solutions to give not rhenium (III) sulphide but a mixture of the disulphide and heptasulphide. Tetravalent rhenium solutions gave the disulphide, and perrhenate solutions gave the heptasulphide. All of the sulphide precipitates were readily converted to perrhenate by hydrogen peroxide solution.

Rhenium could be fairly readily separated from the other elements precipitated by hydrogen sulphide by removing the other elements according to the following scheme[2]

Ag^+	precipitated as AgCl
Hg^{2+}	precipitated as the metal by hydrazine reduction
Pb^{2+}	precipitated as $PbCrO_4$ or 8-hydroxyquinolate
Bi^{3+}	precipitated as BiOCl or $BiPO_4$
Cu^{2+}	precipitated by reduction to the metal
Cd^{2+}	precipitated as 8-hydroxyquinolate

Alternatively the sulphide could be converted to perrhenic acid and the heptaoxide separated by steam distillation.[3] It was found that the best conditions obtained when the solution of perrhenic acid was heated in 80% sulphuric acid to 270–290° and then to introduce steam at such a rate that 100–120 ml of water condensed in an hour. Air or hydrogen chloride was drawn slowly through the solution. About 10 mg of rhenium distilled in 1–5 h. Small quantities of molybdenum, arsenic and antimony also distilled. These could be removed as shown in the scheme below, although the removal of arsenic and antimony was not essential as they did not interfere with the colorimetric determination of rhenium.

As^{5+}	precipitated as $MgNH_4AsO_4 \cdot 6H_2O$
Sb^{5+}	Re_2S_7 precipitated in 7.5 M hydrochloric acid whereas Sb_2S_5 does not precipitate under these conditions
Mo^{6+}	precipitated as 8-hydroxyquinolate

The early separations of technetium used techniques and principles identical to those used in the separation of rhenium. The earliest samples of technetium were prepared from molybdenum by nuclear reactions and the technetium was separated by distillation and sulphide precipitations. Perrier and Segré[4] in their classic paper on the discovery of technetium noted that it behaved very similarly to rhenium and that it followed a rhenium carrier through most of the separations attempted. Thus technetium precipitated as a sulphide with the rhenium, but they discovered it could be separated from rhenium by distillation from sulphuric acid in a stream of hydrogen chloride, rhenium distilled but the technetium did not. It is now known that technetium may be distilled from sulphuric acid solutions under the correct conditions, oxidizing agents such as permanganate, dichromate and nitric acid help the distillation[5] but reducing agents such as hydroxylamine and hydrochloric acid reduce the volatility of the technetium presumably due to reduction to a lower valent non-volatile species.[6]

Technetium heptasulphide has been precipitated with a platinum sulphide carrier and, after dissolving the precipitate, the heptaoxide was distilled from sulphuric acid solution. A cycle of such precipitations and distillations was used to isolate the first weighable amounts of technetium.[7] Technetium heptasulphide has also been coprecipitated with the sulphides of copper, arsenic and iron and after dissolution the technetium was solated in a carrier-free form by ion exchange.[8]

Solvent Extraction

Pyridine extracts rhenium from 4 M sodium hydroxide solutions, the extraction coefficient was found to vary between 30 and 255 according to the conditions used.[9] The extraction of rhenium from perrhenate solutions has been used to separate perrhenates and molybdates quantitatively. Thus 10–100 μg rhenium in solution could be extracted from up to 100 mg molybdenum in one extraction.[10]

The extraction of pertechnetates from alkali solutions with pyridine has also been investigated, Goishi and Libby found an extraction coefficient of 778 from 4 M sodium hydroxide.[9] Later work[11] showed that the extraction coefficient, $d_a°$, varied considerably with the alkali concentration in the aqueous phase, but at no stage was a coefficient as high as 778 observed. Considerably better extraction was obtained using a mixture of sodium hydroxide and sodium carbonate in the aqueous phase. The results are shown in Table 2-1.

Table 2-1. Extraction of technetium by pyridine from aqueous phases

Concentration in aqueous phase (moles/litre)		$d_a°$
NaOH	Na$_2$CO$_3$	
2.0	—	54
3.0	—	239
4.0	—	371
0.5	0.75	98
0.5	1.25	229
0.5	1.75	281

The only other amine that has been used to extract rhenium from aqueous perrhenate solutions is triisooctylamine [tris-(2, 2, 4-trimethylpentyl)amine], but the mechanism of extraction must be different in this case as extraction only occurs in acid solution,[12] while no extraction occurred from neutral or alkaline solutions. By Job's method of continuous variations it was shown that the best extraction occurred when the ratio KReO$_4$: HNO$_3$ was equal to unity, suggesting that it was perrhenic acid which was being extracted. It was also found that the best extraction occurred when the ratio HReO$_4$: R$_3$N was also equal to unity suggesting that the complex formed in the amine phase was HReO$_4$ · R$_3$N.[12]

The extraction of rhenium from aqueous perrhenate solutions by tributylphosphate in an inert organic solvent has been studied. Again extraction did not occur from a neutral potassium perrhenate solution and in acid solution the extraction was most efficient when the ratio $KReO_4$: HNO_3 was unity, suggesting that perrhenic acid was the species extracted.[13] A study of the extraction of rhenium from a solution of perrhenic acid itself gave similar results to those observed for acid potassium perrhenate solutions.[14] The extraction coefficient from perrhenic acid solutions was shown to be independent of rhenium concentration confirming that the same rhenium species was present in both phases. By examining the variation of the extraction coefficient with various low tributylphosphate concentrations in the organic phase (odourless kerosene) a solvation number of three was deduced for perrhenic acid in tributylphosphate.[14] Kertes and Beck[13] obtained a solvation number of four in concentrated solutions of tributylphosphate but it has been claimed that the method of calculating solvation numbers is not valid for concentrated solutions.[15]

The extraction coefficient was found to vary considerably according to the acid in the aqueous phase.[14] Extraction was poor in the presence of nitric and perchloric acids due to competition between these acids and perrhenic acid for tributylphosphate complexing, but the extraction was quite good in sulphuric acid. Some results are given in Table 2-2.

Table 2-2. Extraction of $HReO_4$ by TBP in odourless kerosene[14]

Normality of acid	HNO_3	$HClO_4$	HCl	H_2SO_4
0	0.015	0.015	0.015	0.015
1	0.14	0.031	0.54	0.39
2	0.087	0.007	1.27	0.91
3	0.032	10^{-3}	2.77	1.42
4	0.015	—	5.99	—
5.6	—	—	—	5.65
6	0.0018	—	—	—
7.2	—	—	—	11.5
9	10^{-4}	—	—	18.44
12	10^{-4}	—	—	—

Perrhenic acid was found to be rather weakly extracted from acid solutions by dibutylhydrogenphosphate and in this case a solvation number of three for perrhenic acid in the aqueous phase was observed.[16]

Alcohols, particularly butanol and isoamyl alcohol, were found to extract perrhenic acid from acidified potassium perrhenate solutions.[16] As with tributylphosphate extractions the most efficient extraction was observed with sulphuric acid solutions and poor extraction observed with perchloric and hydrochloric acid solutions. One extraction by isoamyl alcohol from a solution containing perrhenate and molybdate in 3 N sulphuric acid decreased the Mo/Re ratio by a factor of 25.

Small amounts of rhenium have been separated from large quantities of molybdenum by extraction with a chloroform solution of tetraphenylarsonium chloride at pH 8–9. The rhenium was extracted as tetraphenylarsonium perrhenate and the molybdenum did not extract in the pH range used.[17] Tetraphenylphosphonium chloride[18] and triphenylbenzylphosphonium chloride[19] have been used in a similar manner.

In an exhaustive study Boyd and Larson [20, 21] investigated the extraction of technetium from acidic aqueous solutions by over seventy organic compounds. By observing the characteristic absorption of the pertechnetate ion at 2875 Å in both the aqueous and organic phases they proved that the pertechnetate ion was the extracted species. From their wide survey several general points were apparent and are discussed in the following paragraphs.

A necessary condition for efficient extraction by an organic liquid appeared to be the presence of a basic donor atom (oxygen or nitrogen) in the molecule, however the presence of such a donor did not of itself guarantee extraction. The extractant also had to have an appreciable dielectric constant.

The extraction of heptavalent technetium decreased down a homologous series. Correlations between the extraction coefficient and the ratio of the number of oxygen atoms to carbon atoms were found for alcohols, ketones and ethers and a further variation of the extraction coefficient was observed on diluting the organic phase with an inert diluent. The extraction appeared to be a function of the molarity of the donor group in the organic phase.

Measurements of technetium extraction from a number of inorganic acid solutions by cyclohexanol showed that the extraction of technetium decreased as the extraction of the acid increased as was noted for rhenium with tributylphosphate.

Attrep[22] found that for diethyl ether extractions the extraction coefficient for technetium increased with increasing nitric acid concentration in the aqueous phase, varying between 0.029 in 0.5 M nitric acid to 1.098 in 10 M acid.

In later work Boyd and Larson investigated the extraction of technetium in valency states other than seven.[23] Chloro-complexes of technetium (v) in 12 M hydrochloric acid were partially extracted ($d_a°$ approx. 3) by trioctylphosphine oxide but not by diethyl ether. The hexachlorotechnate (iv) ion, $TcCl_6^{2-}$, was extracted from 3 M hydrochloric acid solutions only weakly by 1-pentanol but trioctylphosphine oxide extracted the complex efficiently from 6 M hydrochloric acid.

Ion Exchange

A considerable amount of research has been carried out to investigate the ion exchange behaviour of rhenium and technetium. It has been devoted almost exclusively to studying the separation of molybdenum and rhenium, because of the occurrence of rhenium with molybdenum in nature, and to the separation of technetium and rhenium.

Molybdenum–rhenium separations.—Amberlite IRA-400 was one of the first anion exchange resins used in this field. Fisher and Meloche[24] found that small amounts of perrhenate could be separated from large quantities of molybdate by passing the solution in 2.5 M sodium hydroxide through a column of this resin in the hydroxide form. The molybdenum was held only very weakly and could be eluted with 10% sodium hydroxide solution. After washing the column with water and converting the resin to the chloride form with 0.2 M hydrochloric acid, the rhenium was eluted with 7 M hydrochloric acid. Using this technique 39.6 mg rhenium was separated from 1.422 g molybdenum using 1600 ml 10% sodium hydroxide, 400 ml of water, 200 ml of 0.2 M hydrochloric acid and 1200 ml of 7 M hydrochloric acid. 99.6% of the molybdenum was recovered in the sodium hydroxide and water fractions and 95.4% of the rhenium was recovered from the hydrochloric acid. However the method was slow and tedious taking up to 30 hours and large volumes of reagents were required.

Using the same resin, Amberlite 1RA-400, Meloche and Preuss have improved the efficiency of the separation dramatically.[25] Using a 5 g batch of resin they were able to separate 0.98 mg rhenium from 10.44 g molybdenum (ratio approximately 1:10,000) in a few hours. The solution of perrhenate and molybdate was loaded onto the column in alkali solution, the molybdate being only weakly held and easily eluted with 300 ml of 1 M potassium oxalate solution. After washing the column with 50 ml of water the rhenium was eluted with 300 ml of 1 M perchloric acid in 95–97% yield. A flow rate of up to 2 ml/min was used giving a separation time of about 3 hours.

Dowex-50 anion exchange resin was found to absorb perrhenate from solutions of 0.1–1.0 M hydrochloric acid but molybdate ion was not absorbed under these conditions. Separation was thus possible and, after the molybdenum had been washed from the column, rhenium was eluted using 10% sodium hydroxide solution.

The separation of rhenium and tungsten has been investigated on the micro scale for application to radiochemical separations.[26] A mixture of tungstate and perrhenate in 1 ml of 1.5 M hydrochloric acid solution was passed through a column of Dowex-1 anion exchange resin in the chloride form, the tungsten was weakly held and eluted with 6 ml of the same acid.

The rhenium was then eluted with 4.0 M nitric acid, 93% of the rhenium being recovered in the first 8 ml of solution.

Technetium–rhenium separations.—The first reported separation of technetium and rhenium using anion exchange resins was on the tracer scale.[27] The mixture of technetium and rhenium tracers was prepared by neutron irradiation of molybdenum metal known to contain 2–3 p.p.m. of rhenium, ^{99}Tc and $^{186,\ 188}$Re were produced. After irradiation the metal was dissolved in concentrated sulphuric acid and the heptaoxides distilled. The heptasulphides were precipitated from the distillate and these were finally dissolved in ammonical hydrogen peroxide to give a mixture of pertechnetate and perrhenate ions. This solution was passed through a column of Dowex-2 anion exchange resin in the sulphate form. Both elements were strongly absorbed, rhenium was eluted first with a solution which was 0.1 M in both ammonium sulphate and ammonium thiocyanate and adjusted to pH 8.3–8.5 by the addition of sodium hydroxide. Under these conditions the rhenium was eluted and identified. When the rhenium had been removed the concentration of ammonium sulphate and thiocyanate was increased to 1.0 M at the same pH to quantitatively remove the technetium from the resin. The technetium was found to be better than 99% radiochemically pure.

Sen Sarma and coworkers[28] used Dowex-1 to study the separation of technetium and rhenium. Carrier-free samples of ^{95}Tc and $^{183,\ 184}$Re were prepared by deuteron bombardment of molybdenum and tungsten respectively. The tracers were each purified by distillation and ion exchange and the sulphides were then coprecipitated with copper sulphide. The precipitates were dissolved in ammonical hydrogen peroxide, copper removed by cation exchange resins and the solutions evaporated to dryness. The tracers were then dissolved in water as ammonium pertechnetate and perrhenate. The elution curves for each of the tracers alone showed considerable *tailing* effects after the bulk of the sample had been removed from the resin. This effect could be minimized by refluxing the tracer with dilute sulphuric acid for a few hours before placing on the column, although the reason for this phenomenon was not clear. Solutions of mixtures of the tracers were passed down the column in the perchlorate form and both elements were absorbed. The elements were eluted with either 0.1 M ammonium perchlorate or 0.1 M perchloric acid. Rhenium was removed from the column first and although separations were fairly good some contamination of the technetium by rhenium resulted from the tailing effect. The tailing effect led to a marked discrepancy from the separation factors predicted by plate theories.[29, 30]

Pirs and Magee used the resin Amberlite IRA-400 in the chloride form to investigate the separation of manganese, technetium and rhenium.[31]

Manganese was easily separated by reducing permanganate to the manganese (II) cation which was not absorbed on the anion exchange resin. Mixtures of pertechnetate and perrhenate in 0.1–0.3 M hydrochloric acid were passed through the column and both elements were absorbed. Rhenium was eluted with a 5% solution of ammonium thiocyanate in 0.1–0.2 M hydrochloric acid. After washing the column with water the technetium was eluted with 0.1 M nitric acid. The separation was extremely clean and it was fairly easy to separate 10 μg of technetium from 15 mg of manganese and 0.8 mg of rhenium.

Technetium–molybdenum separations.—The separation of technetium from neutron or deuteron irradiated molybdenum was one of the major problems in the early preparations of technetium. Hall and Johns[32] found that 10 μg of technetium could be separated quantitatively from as much as 50 g of molybdenum in synthetic mixtures using Amberlite IRA-400 anion exchange resin in the perchlorate form.

The irradiated metal was dissolved in a sodium hydroxide–hydrogen peroxide mixture and the solution passed through the column, molybdenum was only weakly absorbed and was removed by eluting with 10% sodium hydroxide solution. Technetium was then eluted with 0.5 M ammonium thiocyanate solution. To recover the technetium the thiocyanate was carefully oxidized with hydrogen peroxide, the solution then boiled to decompose excess peroxide and then made 6–8 N with sulphuric acid. A small amount of platinum was added as a carrier and technetium heptasulphide was then coprecipitated with platinum sulphide.

Technetium may also be recovered quantitatively from molybdenum using Dowex-1 resin in the chloride form.[26] Experiments on the tracer scale showed that molybdate and pertechnetate in 1.0 M hydrochloric acid were absorbed on the resin to different extents. The molybdenum was only weakly held and could be eluted with further quantities of 1.0 M hydrochloric acid. Technetium however was firmly adsorbed under these conditions but it could be readily eluted with 4.0 M nitric acid.

Other Separations

Absorption chromatography.—Molybdenum and rhenium can be separated by absorption chromatography on activated charcoal.[33] Adsorption and desorption of both molybdic and perrhenic acids were first studied separately and, on the basis of the results obtained, a separation of molybdenum and rhenium was attempted. An approximately equimolar mixture of molybdic and perrhenic acids in 1.95 N sulphuric acid was passed down the column of activated charcoal, the molybdenum was only weakly held and it was all (0.43 m moles) eluted with 700 ml of 1.95 N sulphuric acid.

Under these conditions no rhenium was removed from the column but it could be quantitatively recovered with 1200 ml of boiling 0.1 M sodium hydroxide solution. Although this method has now been superseded by ion exchange methods it is of interest as being one of the first successful methods of separating the elements by physical methods.

Electrical methods.—Technetium has been separated from rhenium and molybdenum by electrolysis at a controlled potential.[34] A solution of 0.2 mg of technetium as pertechnetate and similar amounts of perrhenate and molybdate in 2 M sodium hydroxide solution was placed on a platinum foil cathode and electrolysed at 1.1 v (*vs* s.c.e.) for 2 hours. 95% of the technetium was deposited as a black insoluble precipitate which was probably hydrated technetium dioxide, whilst the rhenium and molybdenum remained in solution.

Technetium and rhenium have been separated by paper electrophoresis; it was found that the pertechnetate and perrhenate ions migrated to the anode with the same speed so it was necessary to reduce the elements to lower valency states in the presence of complexing reagents to obtain a reasonable separation.[35] In hydrazine sulphate at pH 8, spots of pertechnetate were rapidly reduced to a black insoluble compound, probably hydrated technetium dioxide, whilst perrhenate remained unaffected and migrated to the anode. The best electrolyte was found to be a mixture of hydrazine hydrate and hydrazine sulphate at pH 9. At 200 volts the following movements were recorded after 90 minutes

$$
\begin{array}{ll}
\text{Tc} & 0 \text{ to } + \ 1 \text{ mm} \\
\text{Re} & -\ 33 \text{ to } -\ 37 \text{ mm} \\
\text{Mo} & -\ 54 \text{ to } -\ 58 \text{ mm}
\end{array}
$$

The spots were compact with no tailing so a good separation was obtained.

Using 1% stannous chloride in 1 M hydrochloric acid as the electrolyte, technetium migrated to the cathode whilst the rhenium either remained on the original spot or migrated to the anode. The separation was complete in 1–2 hours. Addition of 0.2 M tartrate to the solution gave improved separations with the technetium moving to the cathode and all the rhenium migrating to the anode. These observations are interesting because no cationic species have so far been isolated for technetium from aqueous solutions.

Analytical Procedures for Rhenium

There is a wealth of methods for determining rhenium in compounds and minerals. In keeping with the recent trend towards physical methods of analysis there have been many colorimetric methods proposed involving the use of spectrophotometers. Neutron activation analysis has been applied to the problem of determining very small amounts of rhenium in minerals and meteorites. Earlier workers however, determined rhenium by taking advantage of the insolubility of the salts of perrhenic acid with large cations and the ease of oxidation of most valency states of rhenium to perrhenate was utilized with oxidizing agents such as permanganate and ceric salts.

It is not the present intention to give complete experimental details for all the procedures mentioned although this will be done for the more important and widely used methods, so that if necessary a rhenium analysis could be performed using only this text.

Gravimetric methods.—A common method of determining rhenium is by precipitation of sparingly soluble tetraphenylarsonium perrhenate.[36] Rhenium in other valency states can be easily oxidized to perrhenate with mild oxidizing agents prior to the precipitation. It is found that a granular precipitate is obtained if the precipitation is done in the presence of about 0.5 M sodium chloride. Excess tetraphenylarsonium chloride solution is added slowly to the perrhenate solution, keeping volumes to a minimum. The precipitate is allowed to stand overnight then filtered, washed with ice water and finally dried at 110°C. Unfortunately this delightfully simple and accurate method of determining rhenium is open to interference by a large number of other anions particularly permanganate, perchlorate, thiocyanate, iodide, bromide and fluoride. The concentration of nitrate ions must be low and metals which form insoluble chlorides must be absent.

The second common precipitant for the perrhenate ion is nitron[37] (1,4-diphenyl-3,5-*endo*-anilino-4,5-dihydro-1,2,4-triazole). A 5% aqueous solution of nitron acetate is slowly added to the perrhenate solution at 80°, about 0.8 ml of reagent being added for every milligramme of rhenium present. The mixture is allowed to stand in ice water for about $1\frac{1}{2}$ hours. After filtering, the precipitate is washed with ice water and dried at 110°C. The precipitate has the formula $C_{20}H_{16}N_4 \cdot HReO_4$. This method is subject to the same interferences as the previous method.

Perrhenate ion can also be determined gravimetrically by precipitation of thallous perrhenate in 20% acetic acid solution.[38] The precipitate is filtered, washed with glacial acetic acid and dried at 110°C. Halogens interfere with this method which is very rarely used.

A technique which may sometimes prove useful is the precipitation of the hexachlororhenate (IV) anion with tetron (N,N'-tetramethyl-*o*-toluidine) which does not precipitate the perrhenate ion.[39] To a solution of hexachlororhenate (IV) in hydrochloric acid tetron solution is added dropwise with constant stirring at 40–50° until a slight excess is present. The mixture is then cooled in ice and the precipitate filtered and dried at 110°c. Any perrhenate in the filtrate may then be determined using nitron.

Finally, rhenium may be determined gravimetrically by precipitation of the heptasulphide.[40] A perrhenate solution is treated with an alkali sulphide. The resulting salt is decomposed to rhenium heptasulphide in the presence of a large excess of acid. Addition of ammonium sulphate before acidifying the solution is said to make the precipitate granular and easy to filter.

Volumetric methods.—Many lower-valent rhenium compounds may be oxidized to perrhenate by oxidizing agents and either the valency state of the rhenium in the original compound may be deduced, or if this is known the amount of compound present may be found.

Lower oxides of rhenium may be oxidized to perrhenic acid using ferric sulphate in 10% sulphuric acid.[41] The perrhenic acid can be titrated against alkali and the ferrous sulphate titrated against potassium permanganate. This method is not applicable if metallic rhenium is present. Other oxidizing agents such as potassium dichromate and ceric sulphate may be used in similar ways.[42]

Spectrophotometric methods.—The simplest spectrophotometric determination of rhenium involves measuring the absorption due to the perrhenate ion. Headridge[43] has used this method which is said to be particularly suitable for rhenium complexes containing nitrogen since nitrate does not interfere unduly. The absorption maxima of the perrhenate ion were found to be at 228 mμ and 206 mμ with extinction coefficients of 3610 and 6060 respectively. Nitrate absorbs strongly below 264 mμ but it was found possible to make measurements at 258 mμ in the presence of nitrate, at this point the extinction coefficient of perrhenate is 740 and that of nitrate is 2.1. Chloride does not interfere. A standard curve was constructed and found to be a straight line over the range 0–225 p.p.m. rhenium.

Kharlamov *et al*[44] have used this same absorption of the perrhenate ion to determine rhenium in alloys (0.5–17% Re). The alloys were dissolved in hydrochloric acid–nitric acid mixtures and the resulting solutions were evaporated with sulphuric acid to eliminate nitric acid. The pH of the solution was adjusted to 5.5–7.5 and the absorption due to the perrhenate ion was measured. Tungsten, silicon and aluminium did not interfere with the determination nor did molybdenum or vanadium in concentrations up to 5 μg/ml.

Thomason has used the absorption peaks of perrhenate and pertechnetate ions for the simultaneous determination of the two elements.[45]

A combination of the tetraphenylarsonium precipitation method and the spectrophotometric method has been used by Andrew and Gentry.[46]

They precipitated tetraphenylarsonium perrhenate then extracted it into chloroform and measured the absorption due to perrhenate at 255 mμ. The amount of rhenium was determined by comparison with standards.

The absorption of the hexachlororhenate(IV) anion, $ReCl_6^{2-}$, may also be used as the basis for determining rhenium. Perrhenate ion may be reduced quantitatively to this complex using either hydrazine[47] or chromous chloride,[48] the latter being the more rapid reductant. About 7 ml of a solution containing 0.07 to 1.4 mg rhenium are placed in a 50 ml volumetric flask and 25 ml concentrated hydrochloric acid is added. Nitrogen is passed through the solution for a few minutes and then 1 ml of about 0.0045 M chromous chloride is added. After stoppering the flask for a few minutes air is bubbled through the solution which is then diluted to 50 ml and the absorption at 281.5 mμ is measured against a blank which contains all the reagents but no rhenium.

There are several analytical methods which depend upon the reduction of the perrhenate ion, usually by stannous chloride in hydrochloric acid, and the subsequent formation of a colour with a reagent. In most cases the formula of the coloured complex, or even the final oxidation state of the rhenium is unknown, but so long as the intensity of the colour is reproducible under the experimental conditions, this is unimportant.

A typical determination of this type, which in the author's experience has proved to be very reliable, involves the use of furil-α-dioxime.[49] An aliquot of a solution containing 20–300 μg of rhenium is placed in a 50 ml flask. 5 ml of concentrated hydrochloric acid, 13 ml of an acetone solution of furil-α-dioxime (0.70 g/200 ml) and 5 ml of 10% stannous chloride solution are added and the solution is diluted to 50 ml. The red colour forms completely in about 45 minutes and the absorption is then measured at 532 mμ against a blank containing all the reagents but no rhenium. Beer's Law is obeyed within 0.2% in the range 20–300 μg rhenium in 50 ml. This particular method has the very great advantage over other methods of this general type in that no extraction of the complex by an organic solvent is necessary. The major interferences in the method are nitrate, which must be completely absent, and fluoride. Molybdenum interferes but may be readily removed by solvent extraction of its xanthate complex.

The colorimetric method based on the formation of an orange complex with thiocyanate is probably the best known of this type of reaction involving reduction of perrhenate ion with stannous chloride in hydrochloric acid. The colour was first reported by Geilmann et al.[50] The method was first used quantitatively by Hiskey and Meloche[51] to determine the amount of rhenium in molybdenum sulphide ores. They separated the rhenium from the bulk of the molybdenum by distillation from sulphuric acid, but invariably some molybdenum always distilled over. However the

c

interference due to molybdenum was overcome by utilizing the fact that the molybdenum thiocyanate complex decomposes in concentrated hydrochloric acid whilst the rhenium complex was found to be stable. The colour of the rhenium solution was then compared with standards in Nessler tubes.

The method was refined by Malouf and White[52] who also used it to determine rhenium in molybdenum sulphide ores. The sample containing 0.1–0.2 μg of rhenium in the presence of 125 mg of molybdenum was fused with sodium hydroxide–sodium peroxide mixture and after dissolution in water the molybdenum was extracted as its ethylxanthate complex using a benzene–carbon tetrachloride mixture. The rhenium colour was then developed by addition of stannous chloride in hydrochloric acid and sodium thiocyanate. After 30 minutes the coloured complex was extracted with ether and after diluting to 50 ml the absorption of 420 mμ was measured and compared with standards.

A different separation procedure was used by Tarayan and Mushegyan[53] to separate rhenium from molybdenum in ores, although the final determination of the rhenium was similar to the method of Malouf and White. The sample (0.3–3.0 g) was heated with 0.2 g potassium permanganate and 2.0 g calcium oxide at 700° for several hours and the mixture was then extracted with water. The separation of 1–50 μg rhenium from 200–1000 μg molybdenum was accomplished by reducing the molybdate by mercurous nitrate in 1 M sulphuric acid in the presence of thiocyanate to the molybdenum (v) thiocyanate complex which was then extracted with ether. Perrhenate ion is unaffected by this procedure. To the remaining aqueous solution hydrochloric acid and stannous chloride were added and the resulting rhenium thiocyanate complex extracted with butanol.

The thiocyanate method has been applied to the determination of rhenium in ferrous alloys.[54] The alloy was dissolved in hydrochloric acid–nitric acid mixture and the resulting solution evaporated repeatedly with hydrochloric acid to remove nitrate ion. The residue was dissolved in dilute hydrochloric acid and passed through a cation exchanger in the hydrogen form. All of the iron was retained but rhenium passed straight through the column and could be determined directly by the thiocyanate method.

The rhenium content of coal has been determined using the thiocyanate method.[55] The coal (20 g) was mixed with 1 g potassium permanganate and 20 g calcium oxide and the mixture heated at 600° for 6–8 hours. The residue was leached with dilute bromine water and molybdenum removed as its butylxanthate complex by extraction into chloroform. Sodium fluoride was added to complex vanadium and the rhenium then determined by the thiocyanate procedure.

Reduction of perrhenate ion and the subsequent formation of a coloured compound with a complexing agent is the basis of several other methods of determining rhenium. Peshcova and Gromova[56] investigated the colour reactions of several α-dioximes including furil-α-dioxime. They extracted the complexes with organic solvents and found that the following complexes were suitable for rhenium determinations: furil-α-dioxime ($\lambda_{max} = 532$ mμ); o-cyclohexanedionedioxime ($\lambda_{max} = 470$ mμ); dimethylglyoxime ($\lambda_{max} = 450$ mμ) and methylglyoxime ($\lambda_{max} = 440$ mμ).

Kenna[57] has also investigated the colour developed between perrhenate, stannous chloride and dimethylglyoxime in the presence of hydrochloric acid. In this case the complex was not extracted from the aqueous solution and the absorption maximum was found to be at 520 mμ. The colour was found to depend strongly on the rhenium concentration and Beer's Law was not obeyed and comparison had to be made against standards. Iron and molybdenum were found to interfere with the determination.

Rhenium in the concentration range 20–160 μg in 50 ml may be determined using 4-methylnioxime.[58] Perrhenate was reduced using stannous chloride in hydrochloric acid and 4-methylnioxime was added. After five minutes the coloured complex was extracted with chloroform and the optical density measured at 436 mμ and compared with standards.

Diethyldithiophosphoric acid does not react with perrhenate ion at room temperature but on heating or in the presence of stannous chloride an orange compound is formed.[59] It is only sparingly soluble in water but it may be extracted with benzene. The absorption maximum is at 436 mμ, Beer's Law is not obeyed and comparison is made against standards.

The perrhenate ion reacts with thioxin (8-mercaptolquinoline) to form a coloured complex in both acid and alkali solutions.[60] However for the estimation of rhenium it is better to precipitate the complex in 8 M hydrochloric acid as very few other elements form complexes with thioxin at these acidities. The complex can then be extracted with chloroform and its absorption at 438 mμ measured. Molybdenum and tungsten do not interfere.

A similar but even better method is based on the use of the more stable complex formed between perrhenate and o-chloro-8-mercaptolquinoline in 8–12 M hydrochloric acid.[61] This compound has an extinction coefficient of 11,450 at 430 mμ in chloroform. From 5–150 μg rhenium may be determined in the presence of more than 3,000 times as much molybdenum and in the presence of large amounts of tungsten, nickel, cobalt and many other metals.

Up to 50 μg of rhenium in 10 ml of solution may be determined using the colour formed between perrhenate and diphenylthiosemicarbazide in

7 M sulphuric acid solution at 80°.[62] Molybdenum forms a similar complex at first but this rapidly fades and rhenium determination may be made in the presence of large amounts of molybdenum. After heating for 30 minutes the solution is cooled and the coloured complex extracted with chloroform and its absorption at 510 mμ measured.

Other methods.—There are two methods of determining very small amounts of rhenium in minerals and meteorites. The first is based on the observation of Poluektov and coworkers[63, 64] that perrhenate ion catalyses the decomposition of tellurates to tellurium metal in the presence of stannous chloride. The second method is neutron activation analysis.

In determining rhenium by the tellurium method samples are fused with calcium oxide and calcium chloride and magnesium oxide.[63, 64] On leaching, most elements remain as insolubles but rhenium and some molybdenum dissolve. The molybdenum is removed by solvent extraction of its 8-quinolinol complex from almost neutral solution.

To aliquots containing 0.003 to 0.03 μg of rhenium, 2 ml of a *mixed solution*, prepared as described below, and 1 ml of sodium tellurate (0.75% in water) are added and the solution diluted accurately to 5 ml. After standing for 1–5 hours the absorption at 500 mμ is measured and compared with standards. The limit of detection is 0.0002 μg rhenium. Amounts of molybdenum greater than 0.03 μg interfere as do several other elements including platinum, copper and titanium. The *mixed solution* consists of 2.5 ml of tartaric acid solution (50 g/100 ml), 5.2 ml 6 M hydrochloric acid and 1 ml of stannous chlorine solution (375 g in 250 ml of 4 M hydrochloric acid) all diluted to 25 ml.

In the neutron activation method [66, 67] rock samples are irradiated in a nuclear reactor to induce (n, γ) reactions in the rhenium forming ^{186}Re and ^{188}Re. The latter is of short half-life and is allowed to decay before assaying the samples. The rhenium is extracted from the rocks and a rhenium carrier is added to determine the chemical yield of the separation. The radioactivity due to ^{186}Re is then assayed.

Finally rhenium may be determined polarographically using the three electron reduction wave of the perrhenate ion in 4 M perchloric or 4 M hydrochloric acids.[68] This wave is the most accurate for quantitative determination but for detection purposes the eight electron reduction of perrhenate in 2 M potassium chloride solution is the most sensitive.[69]

Analytical Procedures for Technetium

The earliest method of determining technetium was by means of its radioactivity.[4, 70] The method is sensitive and ideal for tracer amounts of those isotopes which have convenient radioactive properties, but for the common isotope ^{99}Tc, even though it has a specific activity of 37,800 disintegrations/min/μg, the method is not suitable for quantitative analysis. The β particles from ^{99}Tc have very low energy ($E_{max} = 0.3$ Mev) and considerable difficulties can arise from back scattering and self absorption effects in the counting samples. Many chemical methods for the determination of technetium are now available, but counting techniques remain a useful method of detecting small amounts of technetium, the limit of detection of ^{99}Tc being about 0.1 μg. Gravimetric methods for determining technetium are very similar to those employed for determining rhenium. The usual precipitants are nitron and tetraphenylarsonium chloride.[71] The methods are open to the same interferences as the rhenium determination and of course cannot be used to determine technetium in the presence of rhenium, but the methods are quite suitable for the analysis of technetium compound. The precipitation of nitron and tetraphenylarsonium pertechnetates are rather more soluble than the rhenium compounds. Comparatively large amounts of technetium are required for these analyses and if the amount of technetium is limited one of the spectrophotometric methods, which require only a few microgrammes of technetium, may be preferable to avoid frequent recycling of the element.

Spectrophotometric methods.—As may be expected some of these methods are similar to those already described for rhenium, but there are also some which are specific for technetium. The simplest spectrophotometric method is based on the measurement of the intensities of the characteristic peaks of the spectrum of the pertechnetate ion. These were found to occur at 2460 Å and 2890 Å ($\epsilon = 6220$ and 2360 respectively).[72] Rhenium does not interfere with the determination, indeed the measurement of these peaks and the corresponding ones for perrhenate (235 mμ) has been used for the simultaneous estimation of the elements.[72]

Technetium has been determined using furil-α-dioxime in a very similar way to the method used for rhenium. The colour formation with technetium was slow and the extinction coefficient was much smaller than for rhenium.[73] The absorption spectrum suggested that two complexes were formed between technetium and furil-α-dioxime but they were always in the same proportion under the experimental conditions and Beer's Law was obeyed. By suitable scaling down of the rhenium procedure analyses could be accurately performed on aliquots containing only 10 μg of technetium. Such small quantities usually need not be recovered from the analytical residues and can be discarded.

The aliquot containing 10–25 μg of technetium was placed in a 10 ml graduated flask and 1 ml concentrated hydrochloric acid was added. 2.5 ml of furil-α-dioxime solution (0.35 g in 100 ml acetone) and 1 ml stannous chloride solution (10 g in 10 ml concentrated hydrochloric acid, diluted to

100 ml) were added and the solution diluted to precisely 10 ml. The colour took about 7 hours to develop, thereafter it was stable for at least 24 hours. The optical density was measured in 4 cm cells at 530 mμ and compared with standards containing known amounts of technetium. Beer's Law was strictly obeyed between 9–50 μg technetium in 10 ml of solution.

Pertechnetate ion is reduced by ammonium thiocyanate in acid solution to give complexes of Tc^V and Tc^{IV}. An analytical method based on the formation of the Tc^V complex has been developed.[74] The technetium solution was adjusted to 3.5–4.0 M sulphuric acid and 0.5 ml of 4.0 M ammonium thiocyanate was added. This was sufficient for both reduction and complexing of the technetium. The reaction was allowed to proceed for 35–45 seconds then 6 ml acetone added and the solution diluted to exactly 10 ml. The maximum colour was developed in 1–3 hours. The optical density was measured at 510 mμ and compared against standards. The thiocyanate method has been modified for the routine analysis of technetium in uranium.[75] 50 ml of a solution containing up to 5 g uranium and 30 mg technetium were placed in a separating funnel, and the acidity adjusted to 2.5–3.5 N. 1 ml of an iron solution (1 g FeCl$_3 \cdot$6H$_2$O in 100 ml) and 5 ml ammonium thiocyanate (500 g in 1 l) and 1 ml ascorbic acid (5 g in 100 ml) were added. Exactly 25 ml of n-butyl acetate were added and the funnel shaken for 30 seconds. The organic layer was washed with sodium dihydrogen phosphate solution to remove iron and the optical density measured in 5 cm cells at 585 mμ if molybdenum is present and at 510 mμ if molybdenum is absent. Molybdenum interferes with the peak at 510 mμ ($\epsilon = 50{,}000$) and in the presence of molybdenum the measurements must be made at 585 mμ ($\epsilon = 16{,}500$).

Thioglycollic acid complexes with the pertechnetate ion to give a green complex with an absorption maximum at 655 mμ.[76] Aliquots of pertechnetate were placed in a 5 ml flask and 1 ml of 1 M sodium acetate and 1 ml of a 10% v/v solution of thioglycollic acid, adjusted to pH 8.0 $\pm$ 0.2, were added. The colour developed in 1 hour at room temperature or in 15 minutes if the flask was heated on the water bath, it was then stable for at least 24 hours. After diluting to exactly 5 ml the optical density was measured at 655 mμ and compared with standards. Beer's Law was obeyed in the range 2–40 μg Tc/ml with $\epsilon = 1800$. The colour was rather dependent upon the pH of the solution, below pH 8.0 a reddish colour developed and above pH the peak intensity was irregular. Of many common ions investigated, including perrhenate, only molybdate, ruthenate and dichromate interfered.

A somewhat similar procedure made use of the complexes formed between pertechnetate and toluene-3,4-dithiol.[77] At least two complexes were formed but by suitable control of factors such as choice of extracting solvent, order of addition of reagents and concentration of reagents, it was found to be possible to evolve a method in which a golden complex (λ_{max} 450 mμ) was formed. The complex was extracted into carbon tetrachloride and the optical density at 450 mμ compared with standards.

10 ml of carbon tetrachloride were placed in a separating funnel. 2 ml of water and 2 ml of reagent (5 g toluene-3,4-dithiol and 12.5 g thioglycollic acid in 1 l of 2.5% w/v sodium hydroxide) were added. An aliquot containing 10–80 μg technetium and 1 ml of concentrated hydrochloric acid was added and the complex extracted by 15 minutes shaking. The carbon tetrachloride was run off and diluted to exactly 10 ml and the optical density measured at 450 mμ. Beer's Law was obeyed in the range 10–80 μg technetium with $\epsilon = 15,000$. Many elements interfered and it was necessary to separate the technetium first. It is not clear from the original paper whether rhenium interferes with this determination.

p-Thiocresol has been used as a reagent for technetium.[78] This reagent reduced pertechnetate ion in glacial acetic acid to a complex thought to contain technetium (v). Rhenium was not reduced under these conditions. The yellowish-brown complex was extracted twice with chloroform and the optical density measured at 410 mμ and compared with standards. After removal of the technetium from the original solution in this way rhenium could be determined using the same reagent with the addition of stannous chlorine as a reducing agent.

Several spot tests for the detection of technetium have been proposed some of which may be suitable for extension to the colorimetric determination of the element.[79] The most promising seemed to be the reactions of pertechnetate with potassium ethylxanthate which gave a purplish-red colour, which was subject to molybdenum interference, and the green colour formed with stannous chloride and dimethylglyoxime.

Other methods.—Three methods, in addition to direct radiochemical assay, are available for the determination of very small amounts of technetium. Neutron activation analysis has been used in an effort to detect naturally occurring ^{98}Tc.[80] Samples were irradiated in a nuclear reactor to induce the reaction ^{98}Tc (n, γ) ^{99m}Tc and a search was made for the activity of the isomeric state of ^{99}Tc which decays to the long-lived ground state with a half-life of about 6 hours. Neutron activation analysis may also be used to determine small amounts of ^{99}Tc by the same method.[81] In this case ^{100}Tc with a half-life of 15.8 seconds is produced but because of its very short half-life special arrangements must be made to ensure that counting can begin a few seconds after removal of the sample from the nuclear reactor.

The arc and spark spectra of neutral technetium atoms and Tc$^+$ ions have been recorded between 8829.80 Å and 2298.10 Å.[82, 83] The strongest lines are given in Table 2-3. It was estimated that the strongest lines would reveal technetium in concentration of the order 10^{-7}.

Table 2-3. Principle lines in the arc and spark spectra of technetium

Wavelength	Intensity	Spectrum
4297.06	500	Tc arc
4262.26	400	Tc arc
4238.19	300	Tc arc
3636.10	400	Tc arc
3237.02	400	Tc$^+$ spark
3212.01	300	Tc$^+$ spark
3195.21	200	Tc$^+$ spark
2647.02	600	Tc$^+$ spark
2610.00	800	Tc$^+$ spark
2543.24	1000	Tc$^+$ spark

Technetium may be determined polarographically by reduction of pertechnetate to Tc^{IV} in a phosphate buffer at pH 7.0[84] or by reduction of pertechnetate in 0.1 M potassium cyanide or 0.1 M potassium hydroxide solution.[69]

References

1. W. GEILMANN, F. WIECHMANN and F. W. WRIGGE, Z. Anal. Chem. **126**, 418 (1944).
2. W. GEILMANN and H. BODE, Z. Anal. Chem. **132**, 250 (1951).
3. W. GEILMANN and H. BODE, Z. Anal. Chem. **130**, 320 (1950).
4. C. PERRIER and G. SEGRE, J. Chem. Phys. **5**, 712 (1937).
5. M. ISHIBASHI, T. FUJINAYA and K. KOYAMA, Nippon Kagaku Ryohogakukai Zasshi **81**, 1260 (1960).
6. M. KOYAMA, Bull. Chem. Soc. Japan **34**, 1766 (1961).
7. G. E. BOYD, Q. V. LARSON and E. E. MOTTA, Unclassified Document A.E.C.D. 251 (1948).
8. N. MATSUURA, K. KOJIMA and A. IGUCHI, Bunseki Kagaku **7**, 792 (1958).
9. W. GOISHI and W. F. LIBBY, J. Am. Chem. Soc. **74**, 6109 (1952).
10. D. T. MESHRI and B. C. HALDAR, J. Sci. Ind. Res. (India) **20B**, 551 (1961).
11. S. J. RIMSHAW and G. F. MALLING, Anal. Chem. **33**, 751 (1961).
12. A. S. KERTES and A. BECK, J. Chem. Soc. 1926 (1961).
13. A. S. KERTES and A. BECK, J. Chem. Soc. 1921 (1961).
14. R. COLTON, U.K.A.E.A. Document, A.E.R.E.-R3823 (1961).
15. E. HESFORD and H. A. C. MCKAY, Trans. Faraday Soc. **54**, 573 (1958).
16. A. S. KERTES and A. BECK, J. Chem. Soc. 5046 (1961).
17. S. TRIBALAT, Anal. Chim. Acta **3**, 113 (1949).

18. S. TRIBALAT, *Anal. Chim. Acta* **4**, 258 (1950).
19. S. TRIBALAT, *Anal. Chim. Acta* **5**, 115 (1951).
20. G. E. BOYD and Q. V. LARSON, *Unclassified Document* O.R.N.L. **2584** (1959).
21. G. E. BOYD and Q. V. LARSON, *J. Phys. Chem.* **64**, 988 (1960).
22. M. ATTREP, *Anal. Chem.* **34**, 1349 (1962).
23. G. E. BOYD and Q. V. LARSON, *Unclassified Document* O.R.N.L. 2782.
24. S. A. FISHER and V. M. MELOCHE, *Anal. Chem.* **24**, 1100 (1952).
25. V. M. MELOCHE and A. F. PREUSS, *Anal. Chem.* **26**, 1911 (1954).
26. E. H. HUFFMAN, R. L. OSWALT and L. A. WILLIAMS, *J. Inorg. Nucl. Chem.* **3**, 49 (1956).
27. R. W. ATTEBURY and G. E. BOYD, *J. Am. Chem. Soc.* **72**, 4805 (1950).
28. R. N. SEN SARMA, E. ANDERS and J. M. MILLER, *J. Phys. Chem.* **63**, 559 (1959).
29. S. W. MAYER and E. R. TOMKINS, *J. Am. Chem. Soc.* **69**, 2866 (1947).
30. E. GLUECKAUF, *Trans. Faraday Soc.* **51**, 34 (1955).
31. M. PIRS and R. J. MAGEE, *Talanta* **8**, 395 (1961).
32. N. F. HALL and D. H. JOHNS, *J. Am. Chem. Soc.* **75**, 5787 (1953).
33. G. B. ALEXANDER, *J. Am. Chem. Soc.* **71**, 3043 (1949).
34. L. B. ROGERS, *J. Am. Chem. Soc.* **71**, 1507 (1949).
35. R. A. G. DE CARVALLO, *Proc. Intern. Conf. Peaceful Uses Energy Geneva* **28**, 97 (1955).
36. H. H. WILLARD and G. M. SMITH, *Ind. Eng. Chem.* **11**, 305 (1939).
37. W. GEILMANN and A. VOIGHT, *Z. Anorg. Allgem. Chem.* **193**, 311 (1930).
38. F. KRAUSS and H. STEINFELD, *Z. Anorg. Allgem. Chem.* **197**, 52 (1931).
39. W. GEILMANN and L. C. HURD, *Z. Anorg. Allgem. Chem.* **213**, 336 (1933).
40. I. K. TAIMNI and G. B. S. SALARIA, *Anal. Chim. Acta* **12**, 519 (1955).
41. W. GEILMANN and L. C. HURD, *Z. Anorg. Allgem. Chem.* **210**, 350 (1933).
42. W. GEILMANN and L. C. HURD, *Z. Anorg. Allgem. Chem.* **222**, 56 (1935).
43. J. B. HEADRIDGE, *Analyst* **83**, 690 (1958).
44. I. P. KHARLAMOV, P. Y. YAKOLEV and M. I. LYKOVA, *Zavodsk. Lab.* **27**, 141 (1961).
45. P. F. THOMSON, *Unclassified Document* O.R.N.L. 1880.
46. T. R. ANDREW and C. H. R. GENTRY, *Analyst* **82**, 372 (1957).
47. R. J. MEYER and C. L. RULFS, *Anal. Chem.* **27**, 387 (1955).
48. V. M. MELOCHE and R. L. MARTIN, *Anal. Chem.* **28**, 1671 (1956).
49. V. M. MELOCHE, R. L. MARTIN and W. H. WEBB, *Anal. Chem.* **29**, 527 (1957).
50. W. GEILMANN, F. W. WRIGGE and F. WEIBKE, *Z. Anorg. Allgem. Chem.* **208**, 217 (1932).
51. C. F. HISKEY and V. M. MELOCHE, *Ind. Eng. Chem.* **12**, 503 (1940).
52. E. E. MALOUF and M. G. WHITE, *Anal. Chem.* **23**, 497 (1951).
53. V. M. TARAYAN and L. G. MUSHEGYAN, *Izv. Akad. Nauk Arm. SSR Khim. Nauki.* **11**, 397 (1959).
54. D. I. RYABCHIKOV and A. I. LAZAREV, *Zh. Analit. Khim.* **16**, 366 (1961).
55. V. V. KUZNETSOVA, *Zh. Analit. Khim.* **16**, 736 (1961).
56. V. M. PESHCOVA and M. I. GROMOVA, *Vestn. Mosk. Univ. Ser. I, Fiz. Nat. i Estesteven Nauk* **85** (1952).
57. B. T. KENNA, *Anal. Chem.* **33**, 1130 (1961).
58. J. L. KASSNER, S. F. TING and E. L. GROVE, *Talanta* **7**, 269 (1961).
59. A. I. LAZAREV and V. V. RODZAEVSKII, *Zh. Analit. Khim.* **16**, 243 (1961).
60. J. BANKOVSKIS, A. IEVINS and E. LUKSA, *Zh. Analit. Khim.* **14**, 714 (1959).

61. J. BANKOVSKIS and E. LABAUOVA, *Latvijas PSR Zinatnu Akad. Vestis* **1**, 97 (1960).
62. W. GEILMANN and R. NEEB, *Z. Anal. Chem.* **151**, 401 (1956).
63. N. S. POLUEKTOV, *J. Appl. Chem. USSR* **14**, 695 (1941).
64. N. S. POLUEKTOV and L. I. KONONENKO, *Zavodsk. Lab.* **25**, 548 (1959).
65. F. O. SIMON and F. S. GRIMALDI, *Anal. Chem.* **34**, 1361 (1962).
66. E. D. GOLDBERG and H. BROWN, *Anal. Chem.* **22**, 308 (1950).
67. D. F. C. MORRIS and F. W. FIFIELD, *Talanta* **8**, 612 (1961).
68. J. J. LINGANE, *J. Am. Chem. Soc.* **64**, 1001 (1942).
69. R. COLTON, J. DALZIEL, W. P. GRIFFITH and G. WILKINSON, *J. Chem. Soc.* 71 (1960).
70. C. PERRIER and E. SEGRE, *J. Chem. Phys.* **7**, 155 (1939).
71. G. W. PARKER and W. J. MARTIN, *Unclassified Document* O.R.N.L. 870.
72. J. WOLKOWITZ, *Unclassified Document* O.R.N.L. 1880.
73. R. COLTON and H. MORLEY, *U.K.A.E.A. Document* A.E.R.E.-R3746 (1961).
74. C. E. CROUTHAMEL, *Anal. Chem.* **29**, 1756 (1957).
75. O. H. HOWARD and C. W. WEBER, *Anal. Chem.* **34**, 530 (1962).
76. F. J. MILLER and P. F. THOMASON, *Anal. Chem.* **32**, 1429 (1960).
77. F. J. MILLER and P. F. THOMASON, *Anal. Chem.* **33**, 404 (1961).
78. M. AL-KAYSSI and R. J. MAGEE, *Talanta* **10**, 1047 (1963).
79. F. JASMIN, R. J. MAGEE and C. L. WILSON, *Talanta* **2**, 93 (1959).
80. E. ALPEROVITCH and J. M. MILLER, *Nature* **176**, 299 (1955).
81. G. E. BOYD and Q. V. LARSON, *J. Phys. Chem.* **60**, 707 (1956).
82. W. F. MEGGERS and B. F. SCRIBENER, *J. Res. Nat. Bur. Stds. A.* **45**, 476 (1950).
83. W. F. MEGGERS, *Spectrochim. Acta* **4**, 317 (1951).
84. G. E. BOYD, *J. Chem. Educ.* **36**, 3 (1959).

3

Oxides, Oxygen Anions and Sulphides

There are three well-established oxides for rhenium and so far only two for technetium. As is typical for second and third transition elements in this part of the periodic table the maximum oxidation state of the elements is very stable in the oxygen compounds. The heptaoxides are the products formed by heating the elements, or lower oxides, in oxygen. They dissolve in water to give perrhenic and pertechnic acids respectively, these are strong acids which give rise to extensive series of salts. In contrast to the permanganates they are colourless, the perrhenates have virtually no oxidizing power and the pertechnetates very little. The perrhenates of the alkali metals are remarkably stable towards heat, indeed it has been reported that potassium perrhenate may be distilled at 1400° without decomposition. The solubilities of the perrhenates in water closely parallel those of the perchlorates, thus sodium perrhenate is readily soluble in both hot and cold water, but potassium perrhenate is quite soluble in hot water and only very sparingly soluble in cold water. The useful property of solubility in organic solvents shown by many perchlorates is not shared by the perrhenates. In general the pertechnetates are rather more soluble in water than the corresponding perrhenates.

The rhenates derived from rhenium trioxide are rather unstable. In solution they disproportionate and can only be prepared by fusion methods. Neither technetium trioxide nor the technates have yet been prepared.

The dioxides may be obtained anhydrous or in the hydrated form, they closely resemble the dioxides of molybdenum and ruthenium.

The sulphides are of relatively little importance except for catalytic purposes and insofar as rhenium usually occurs as a sulphide associated with molybdenum disulphide ores. Recently some interesting reactions involving the chlorination of rhenium sulphides have yielded some unusual rhenium compounds.

Oxygen Compounds

Rhenium heptaoxide.—Rhenium heptaoxide is the product obtained by treating rhenium metal with excess oxygen above 150°.[1] It was also claimed that a higher oxide, rhenium octaoxide, is formed in the reaction,[1] but this observation has never been confirmed by other workers.[2] If the reaction between rhenium metal and oxygen is carried out in a flow system much of the oxide is produced in the form of a very fine smoke which is extremely difficult to condense. It is usual to perform the oxidation in a static system, an excellent arrangement has been described by Melaven and coworkers.[3]

Other methods of preparation of the heptaoxide include evaporation of a solution of perrhenic acid under vacuum followed by sublimation, and the action of oxygen at elevated temperatures on lower oxides and the sulphides of rhenium.

Rhenium heptaoxide is a pale yellow crystalline solid. The complete structure of the solid is not known although the unit cell has been shown to have the following dimensions[4]

$$a = 15.25 \pm 0.1 \text{ Å}$$

$$b = 5.48 \pm 0.02 \text{ Å}$$

$$c = 12.5 \pm 0.1 \text{ Å}$$

$$V = 1044 \text{ Å}^3$$

The density of 6.10 g/c.c. suggested that there were eight formula units in the unit cell.

The melting point of rhenium heptaoxide was originally given[1] as 220°, but later results have shown that it melts at about 300°.[2, 5, 6] Traces of water have been shown to depress the melting point by as much as 150° and this must be the most probable cause of the low melting point originally quoted.

Rhenium heptaoxide is extremely hygroscopic and very soluble in water to form perrhenic acid, $HReO_4$. The heptaoxide is reduced to lower oxides by carbon monoxide and sulphur dioxide at high temperature. Hydrogen reduces it to the dioxide at 300° and to the metal itself at 800°.[1] The heptaoxide also reacts with dry hydrogen sulphide to give rhenium heptasulphide.[1]

The vapour pressure of rhenium heptaoxide as a function of temperature has been measured twice,[5, 6] the discrepancy between the results being less than 2%. The plot of log $p_{(Re_2O_7)}$ against $1/T$ was a straight line, the equations being

$$\log p = \frac{-7218}{T} + 14.839 \quad \text{(Ogawa)}$$

Solid Re_2O_7

$$\log p = \frac{-7320}{T} + 15.010 \quad \text{(Smith } et\ al\text{)}$$

$$\log p = \frac{-3920}{T} + 9.047 \quad \text{(Ogawa)}$$

Liquid Re_2O_7

$$\log p = \frac{-3868}{T} + 8.98 \quad \text{(Smith } et\ al\text{)}$$

Thermodynamic functions derived from these results are shown in Table 3-1.

Table 3-1. Thermodynamic properties of rhenium heptaoxide

Property	Ogawa[5]	Smith et al[6]
Melting point	297°	300.3°
Boiling point	363°	360.3°
ΔH_{sub}	33.05 kcal/mole	33.5 kcal/mole
ΔS_{sub}	—	58.4 cal/mole/deg
ΔH_{fus}	14.61 kcal/mole	15.81 kcal/mole
ΔS_{fus}	—	27.6 cal/mole/deg
ΔH_{vap}	17.95 kcal/mole	17.7 kcal/mole
ΔS_{vap}	—	28.0 cal/mole/deg

The heat of formation of rhenium heptaoxide has also been measured twice.[7, 8] Values of -297.5 ± 2.0 kcal/mole[7] and -295.9 ± 2.0 kcal/mole[8] were obtained and the mean of these results, -296.7 kcal/mole has been recommended as the best value.[8]

The low temperature heat capacity of rhenium heptaoxide has been measured in order to calculate values for the entropy and free energy functions.[9] The entropy of solid rhenium heptaoxide was found to be 49.54 cal/mole/deg and combined with the data in Table 3-1 a value of 105.0 ± 0.3 cal/mole/deg was derived as the entropy of rhenium heptaoxide as an ideal gas at one atmosphere pressure at $298.16°K$. Similarly a combination of the heat of formation of rhenium heptaoxide[7, 8] with the entropy of formation gave a value of -255.0 ± 2.0 kcal/mole for the free energy of formation of rhenium heptaoxide.

Technetium heptaoxide.—Technetium heptaoxide was the only product when technetium metal was heated in excess of oxygen.[10] It was shown that the compound was the heptaoxide by dissolving it in water and potentiometrically titrating the solution against ammonia solution, a curve typical of a strong monobasic acid was obtained. Furthermore, the weight of ammonium pertechnetate obtained by evaporation of the solution agreed with that expected if the oxide were the heptaoxide.

Technetium heptaoxide is a pale yellow crystalline solid; it is not isostructural with rhenium heptaoxide, apparently being of lower symmetry.[11] Like its rhenium analogue it is very hygroscopic, dissolving in water to form pertechnic acid, $HTcO_4$. The melting point is 119.5° and the boiling point has been estimated from vapour pressure measurements to be 311°. The liquid range of technetium heptaoxide is thus far greater than that of rhenium heptaoxide. A peculiar difference has been found between the electrical conductivities of the heptaoxides of technetium and rhenium. Solid technetium heptaoxide conducted electricity but the melt did not, for rhenium heptaoxide the reverse was true, the solid did not conduct electricity but the melt did.[12]

The vapour pressure of technetium heptaoxide has been measured as a function of temperature, the results could be fitted to the following equations[12]

$$\text{Solid } Tc_2O_7 \quad \log p = \frac{-7205}{T} + 18.279$$

$$\text{Liquid } Tc_2O_7 \quad \log p = \frac{-3571}{T} + 8.999$$

The melting point derived by simultaneous solution of these equations is 118.4° in fair agreement with the experimentally observed value of 119.5°. The boiling point calculated from the liquid vapour pressure curve is 310.6°, a value which has been confirmed by direct observation.[13]

The heat of formation of technetium heptaoxide has been determined as 266 ± 2.6 kcal/mole, and the heat of solution of technetium heptaoxide to give pertechnic acid was found to be 11.59 ± 0.08 kcal/mole.[14]

Perrhenic acid and the perrhenates.—Rhenium heptaoxide dissolves in water to form a colourless solution of perrhenic acid, $HReO_4$. Solutions of perrhenic acid may also be prepared by dissolution of rhenium powder in hydrogen peroxide, bromine water[15] or nitric acid. Anodic oxidation of the consolidated metal (which does not dissolve in hydrogen peroxide) in alkali hydroxide gives a perrhenate solution from which the free acid may be obtained by the use of a cation exchanger.[16] Many compounds of rhenium including sulphides, lower oxides and some complexes may be oxidized to solutions of perrhenic acid with nitric acid.

Perrhenic acid is a strong acid as is qualitatively shown by its behaviour on ion exchange resins, its attack on metals such as magnesium and zinc and on metal oxides and carbonates, and the pH of its solutions. Quantitatively it has been shown to be a strong acid by measuring its heat of neutralization[7] (13.5 kcal/mole) and its dissociation constant which is about 40.[17]

On evaporation the colourless solution of perrhenic acid becomes yellowish and viscous. Additional lines appear in the Raman spectrum presumably due to the undissociated acid itself, but neither the acid nor its hydrates have been isolated, in contrast to pertechnic acid which has been isolated. Further evaporation of the solution leads to volatilization of rhenium heptaoxide. The extraction of rhenium from acid solutions of perrhenates by certain organic solvents has been shown to be due to the extraction of perrhenic acid.[18, 19]

Perrhenic acid is very stable and shows little oxidizing power. However it can be reduced by various amalgams and hydrazine. Hydrochloric acid causes slow reduction, but this is probably due to substitution reactions which will be discussed in another section.

The perrhenates are usually white crystalline compounds, the alkali perrhenates have either a scheelite (tetragonal) structure or a pseudo-scheelite (orthorhombic) structure with the unit cell dimensions given in Table 3-2.

Table 3-2. Unit cell dimensions of some simple perrhenates

Compound	a	b	c
$NaReO_4$	5.362 ± 0.001	—	11.718 ± 0.002
NH_4ReO_4	5.871 ± 0.003	—	12.942 ± 0.007
$RbReO_4$	5.803 ± 0.003	—	13.167 ± 0.007
$TlReO_4$ (above 123°)	5.761 ± 0.005	—	13.33 ± 0.01
$CsReO_4$	5.737 ± 0.003	5.968 ± 0.003	14.241 ± 0.007
$TlReO_4$ (below 123°)	5.623 ± 0.003	5.791 ± 0.003	13.295 ± 0.007

The radius of the Re^{7+} ion has been estimated as 0.56 Å from a consideration of ionization potentials.[21]

From a study of the infra-red and Raman spectra of solutions of perrhenic acid and sodium perrhenate Claasson and Zielen[22] concluded that the perrhenate ion exists in solution as the tetrahedral ReO_4^- ion and not as the octahedral ReO_6^{5-} ion as had been previously suggested from a study of the Raman spectrum.[23] Raman peaks were observed at 971, 918 and 331 cm^{-1} and an infra-red absorption (attributable to the Re$=$O stretch) was observed at 914 cm^{-1}. A similar value, 913 cm^{-1}, has been reported by other workers.[24]

Potassium perrhenate is the most frequently encountered compound of rhenium. It is a white crystalline material which is only sparingly soluble in cold water but quite soluble in hot water. It is even less soluble in alkali solutions but rather more soluble in acid solution. The convenient solubility properties of potassium perrhenate together with the ease of oxidizing most rhenium compounds to perrhenate, make it an ideal form in which to recover rhenium from natural sources or laboratory residues. The solubilities and other properties of some simple perrhenates are given in Table 3-3.[25]

Table 3-3. Physical properties of some simple perrhenates

Compound	M.p.(°c)	Density	Solubility (moles/100 g $H_2O \times 10^2$)			Heat of solution (kcal/mole)
			0°	30°	50.3°	
$LiReO_4.2H_2O$	87.5	3.69	100	140	140	1.6
$LiReO_4$	426	4.61	—	—	—	—
$NaReO_4$	414	5.24	37.8	53.2	63.6	1.83
$KReO_4$	555	4.38	0.124	0.508	1.11	7.68
NH_4ReO_4	decomp.	7.53	1.03	3.25	5.99	6.21
$RbReO_4$	598	4.73	0.116	0.468	1.05	7.70
$CsReO_4$	616	4.76	0.0861	0.287	0.640	7.69

The density of potassium perrhenate solutions is given by the equation[26]

$$d_{KReO4} = 0.99707 + 0.2330\,m$$

where m = concentration of $KReO_4$ in moles/1000 g solution. The variation of equivalent conductivity with concentration for potassium perrhenate has been investigated[26] and the limiting conductance at infinite dilution was found to be 128.20 Ω^{-1}.

The low temperature heat capacity of potassium perrhenate has been measured between 16–300°K.[27] There was no indication of any phase transition in the temperature range studied. From the combination of the observed heat capacities and solubility and heat of solution measurements[7] thermodynamic functions for potassium perrhenate were calculated as a function of temperature.

Although the alkali metal perrhenates are the most common salts of perrhenic acid, many other perrhenates have been prepared, these are shown in Table 3-4.

In most cases the salts were prepared by dissolving the metal oxide, carbonate or hydroxide in perrhenic acid, although in the case of thallous perrhenate double decomposition between thallous sulphate and potassium perrhenate was used. In no case was a melting point recorded for a hydrated salt as they all lost water more or less readily. Three perrhenates showed transition points on their cooling curves: $Ca(ReO_4)_2$ at 778°, $Sr(ReO_4)_2$ at 788° and $Hg(ReO_4)_2$ at 405°.

Table 3-4. Properties of some perrhenates

Compound	Colour	M.p. °C	Solubility (g/100 g H_2O)			Density (gm/cc)	Ref.
			0°	30°	50°		
$Mg(ReO_4)_2$	white	930	—	283.6	—	5.01	28
$Mg(ReO_4)_2 \cdot 4H_2O$	white	—	—	527.7	—	3.51	28
$Ca(ReO_4)_2$	white	934	—	187.0	—	4.94	28
$Ca(ReO_4)_2 \cdot 2H_2O$	white	—	—	227.8	—	4.95	28
$Sr(ReO_4)_2$	white	884	—	110.1	—	4.95	28
$Sr(ReO_4)_2 \cdot H_2O$	white	—	—	117.5	—	—	28
$Sr(ReO_4)_2 \cdot 2H_2O$	white	—	—	125.3	—	4.82	28
$Ba(ReO_4)_2$	white	799	1.52	8.13	21.51	5.91	28
$Ba(ReO_4)_2 \cdot 4H_2O$	white	—	1.69	9.13	24.54	4.13	28
$Zn(ReO_4)_2$	white	701	—	313.6	—	5.46	28
$Zn(ReO_4)_2 \cdot 4H_2O$	white	—	—	588.4	—	3.75	28
$Cd(ReO_4)_2$	white	624	—	497.5	—	5.99	28
$Cd(ReO_4)_2 \cdot 2H_2O$	white	—	—	743.9	—	4.95	28
$Hg(ReO_4)_2$	white	431	—	—	—	6.95	28
$Hg(ReO_4)_2 \cdot 2H_2O$	white	—	—	—	—	5.62	28
$Cu(ReO_4)_2$	white	—	—	210.4	—	—	28
$Cu(ReO_4)_2 \cdot 4H_2O$	blue	—	—	324.5	—	3.73	28
$Pb(ReO_4)_2$	white	562	4.14	14.81	29.63	6.93	28
$Pb(ReO_4)_2 \cdot 2H_2O$	white	—	4.36	15.67	31.61	5.16	28
$Cu_2(ReO_4)_2$	brown-pink	380	—	—	—	5.70	29
$AgReO_4$	white	455	0.43	1.39	2.71	6.96	29
$TlReO_4$	white	525	0.115	0.298	0.555	6.89	29
$Hg_2(ReO_4)_2$	white	561	—	—	—	7.23	29
$Co(ReO_4)_2$	purple	816	—	299*	—	5.33	30
$Co(ReO_4)_2 \cdot 3H_2O$	pink-red	—	—	462*	—	—	30
$Co(ReO_4)_2 \cdot 4H_2O$	pink-red	—	—	548*	—	3.90	30
$Ni(ReO_4)_2$	yellow	—	—	310*	—	—	30
$Ni(ReO_4)_2 \cdot 2H_2O$	light green	—	—	408*	—	—	30
$Ni(ReO_4)_2 \cdot 4H_2O$	green	—	—	567*	—	3.95	30
$Mn(ReO_4)_2$	pink	861	—	340*	—	5.12	30
$Mn(ReO_4)_2 \cdot 2H_2O$	pink	—	—	464*	—	4.32	30
$Fe(ReO_4)_2$	dark red	—	—	233*	—	—	30
$Fe(ReO_4)_2 \cdot 4H_2O$	orange	—	—	355*	—	3.64	30
$Fe(ReO_4)_3$	black	—	—	270*	—	—	30
$Fe(ReO_4)_3 \cdot 2H_2O$	black	—	—	318*	—	—	30
$Fe(ReO_4)_3 \cdot 4H_2O$	purple	—	—	376*	—	4.13	30

* Signifies solubility measured at 27°.

In addition to the simple metal perrhenates listed in Table 3-4 several perrhenates of metal–ammine cations have been prepared,[31] for example salts of $[Co(NH_3)_6]^{3+}$ and $[Cr(NH_3)_6]^{3+}$ but these are of little importance. On the other hand the insoluble perrhenates formed with nitron and the

D

tetraphenylarsonium cation are of considerable importance for the gravimetric determination of rhenium.

Trimethylsilyl perrhenate is the only ester of perrhenic acid known.[32] It was prepared in good yield by the interaction of either rhenium hepta-oxide and trimethylsilyl oxide or silver perrhenate and trimethylsilicon chloride. It is a white solid m.p. 79.5° and it may be sublimed in a vacuum.

Scharnow claimed to have prepared barium mesoperrhenate $Ba_3(ReO_5)_2$ by the evaporation of an aqueous solution of barium perrhenate, $Ba(ReO_4)_2$, with excess barium hydroxide under an atmosphere of carbon dioxide.[33]

The mixed metal oxides $Ba(Na_{0.5}Re_{0.5})O_3$ and $Ba(Li_{0.5}Re_{0.5})O_3$ containing Re^{VII} have recently been synthesized.[34] These were prepared by the following reactions

$$2\,BaCO_3 + NaReO_4 \rightarrow 2\,Ba(Na_{0.5}Re_{0.5})O_3 + 2\,CO_2$$

$$4\,BaCO_3 + Na_2CO_3 + 2\,NH_4ReO_4 \rightarrow 4\,Ba(Na_{0.5}Re_{0.5})O_3 + 5\,CO_2 + NH_3 + H_2O$$

$$8\,BaCO_3 + 2\,Na_2CO_3 + 4\,Re + 7\,O_2 \rightarrow 8\,Ba(Na_{0.5}Re_{0.5})O_3 + 10\,CO_2$$

The latter method was usually the best but some barium mesoperrhenate was usually also formed. The compounds were red when hot and yellow when cold. X-ray diffraction data fitted a face-centred cubic lattice of the Perovskite type and this is the first example of rhenium displaying six coordination in the heptavalent state.

Feit[35] claimed that the action of hydrogen sulphide on potassium perrhenate gave potassium thioperrhenate, $KReO_3S$, which was said to decompose on standing to give potassium perrhenate and potassium tetrathioperrhenate, $KReS_4$. It was said that this latter compound could be precipitated by addition of thallous nitrate solution and that further treatment of the remaining solution with hydrogen sulphide gave a pure solution of potassium thioperrhenate from which several thioperrhenates were isolated.

Briscoe and coworkers[36] could not confirm potassium tetrathioper-rhenate but they were able to isolate thallous thioperrhenate according to Feit's instructions.[37] No further work has been reported on this system since 1932 and the problem merits further investigation.

Pertechnic acid and the pertechnetates.—Technetium heptaoxide dissolves in water to form pertechnic acid which, in contrast to its rhenium analogue, can be isolated. On evaporating a concentrated solution of pertechnic acid to dryness it became first pink, then red and finally very dark red needles crystallized out. The weight of the crystals showed them to be $Tc_2O_7 \cdot H_2O$ or anhydrous $HTcO_4$.[10] The dissociation pressure of anhydrous pertechnic acid according to the equation

$$HTcO_4(c) \rightleftharpoons \tfrac{1}{2} H_2O(g) + \tfrac{1}{2} Tc_2O_7(c)$$

was found to fit the equation[12]

$$\log p = \frac{-2395}{T} + 8.207$$

The experimental results for the vapour pressure of a saturated solution of pertechnic acid[12] followed a very similar equation

$$\log p = \frac{-2375}{T} + 8.201$$

The heat of formation of pertechnic acid has been calculated as -173.0 ± 1.7 kcal/mole based on determination of the heat of formation of technetium heptaoxide, the heat of solution of the oxide and the heat of dilution of pertechnic acid.[14]

The oxidation potential of the $TcO_2 - TcO_4{}^-$ electrode was found to be -0.782 ± 0.011 v in acid solution.[14]

An oxidation–reduction diagram for acid solutions has been proposed[14]

$$
\begin{array}{ccccccc}
 & & \multicolumn{5}{c}{-0.782} \\
 & 0.240 & & -0.8 & & -0.7 & \\
Tc & \rule{1cm}{0.4pt} & TcO_2 & \rule{1cm}{0.4pt} & TcO_3 & \rule{1cm}{0.4pt} & TcO_4{}^- \\
 & & \multicolumn{5}{c}{-0.472}
\end{array}
$$

Later work[38] has shown that this potential diagram is not accurate because of the presence of oxygen in the solution when measuring the $TcO_2 - TcO_4{}^-$ potential. The new diagram proposed is

$$
\begin{array}{ccccccc}
 & & \multicolumn{5}{c}{-0.738} \\
 & -0.272 & & -0.8 & & -0.7 & \\
Tc & \rule{1cm}{0.4pt} & TcO_2 & \rule{1cm}{0.4pt} & TcO_3 & \rule{1cm}{0.4pt} & TcO_4{}^- \\
 & & \multicolumn{5}{c}{-0.472}
\end{array}
$$

A curve typical of a strong monobasic acid resulted from the potentiometric titration of pertechnic acid with ammonia.[10] So far no evidence has been found for the existence of an ion corresponding to the mesoperrhenate ion $ReO_5{}^{3-}$.

Comparatively few pertechnetates have been described, but those which have been prepared resemble in general the perrhenates although they are usually rather more soluble. Ammonium, potassium and silver pertechnetates have been shown to be isostructural with their rhenium analogues.[39] The radius of the Tc^{7+} ion has been estimated to be 0.56 Å, a value identical with that estimated for rhenium.[21]

Potassium pertechnetate is a white crystalline solid which is considerably more soluble than potassium perrhenate (21.3 g/1000 g at 25°).[40] It is very stable thermally. It undergoes a reversible colour change on heating becoming brilliant yellow at 500°c although some yellow colour is evident at 200°c.[41] It melts at 540° and sublimes unchanged at about 1000°.[41]

Ammonium pertechnetate is a white crystalline solid. Reduction of this compound by hydrogen provides the best method of preparing pure technetium metal.[44]

The pertechnetate ion absorbs strongly in the ultraviolet region with the two main peaks at 2440 and 2875 Å (ϵ = 6220 and 2360 respectively).[41, 45]

The integral heat of solution of potassium pertechnetate has been measured as a function of temperature.[40] The results are given in Table 3-5.

Table 3-5. Heat of solution of potassium pertechnetate

Heat of solution (cal)	Concentration (mole)
12,735	0.02592
12,749	0.02541
12,777	0.01572
12,818	0.00560
12,746	0.00476

Extrapolation to infinite dilution gives

$$\Delta H_{25}^{\circ} = 12,765 \pm 15 \text{ cal/mole}$$

Using estimated activities the entropy of the (TcO_4^- aq) ion was calculated to the 47.9 $\pm$ 0.3 cal/deg/mole.

The crystal structures of several simple pertechnetates have been determined. The ammonium,[42] sodium,[43] potassium[42] and silver[43] salts are all tetragonal with the scheelite structure and isomorphous with the corresponding perrhenates. Caesium pertechnetate is orthorhombic[42] and again isomorphous with the corresponding perrhenate. The unit cell dimensions are given in Table 3-6.

Table 3-6. Unit cell dimensions of some simple pertechnetates

	a (Å)	b (Å)	c (Å)
NH_4TcO_4	5.790	—	13.310
$NaTcO_4$	5.339	—	11.869
$KTcO_4$	5.654	—	13.03
$AgTcO_4$	5.319	—	11.875
$CsTcO_4$	5.718	5.918	14.304

Rhenium trioxide.—All preparations of rhenium trioxide involve the reduction of the heptaoxide. One of the earliest methods used rhenium dioxide as the reductant[46]

$$ReO_2 + Re_2O_7 \rightarrow 3\ ReO_3$$

The trioxide was also prepared in a similar manner by treating the heptaoxide with rhenium metal in a sealed tube at 250°. Excess of the heptaoxide was present to prevent reduction to rhenium dioxide.[47] The compound claimed[48] to have been rhenium pentaoxide, Re_2O_5, formed by the reduction of rhenium heptaoxide by sulphur dioxide was almost certainly the trioxide since it had all the chemical and physical properties now associated with the trioxide. Rhenium heptaoxide may be reduced almost quantitatively to the trioxide with carbon monoxide, but the reaction is slow.[49]

Most of the methods for preparing rhenium trioxide are rather slow and tedious and in some cases the product may be contaminated by lower oxides. In recent years a rather novel preparation has been described for which yields up to 98% have been claimed.[50, 51] Rhenium heptaoxide was dissolved in dioxan and the solution was then cooled in ice. A white crystalline mass, whose composition approximated to $Re_2O_7 \cdot 3C_4H_8O$, was obtained. After decanting off the supernatant liquid the crystals were dried at room temperature and then heated in a crucible on a hot plate. The crystals melted and decomposed leaving chemically pure rhenium trioxide, all of the other products of the pyrolysis (dioxan, aldehydes, carbon monoxide and carbon dioxide) being volatile.

Rhenium trioxide is a red solid although various other colours have been reported. It is strongly dichroic appearing green by transmitted light when in thin films. It is chemically inert. Heating to 110° in air for four hours caused no change.[50] It is not attacked by either dilute or concentrated hydrochloric acid, but it does dissolve in oxidizing acids and alkaline hydrogen peroxide solutions to give the perrhenate ion. With fused alkalis in the absence of air rhenium trioxide gives rhenates. Above 300° in a vacuum rhenium trioxide decomposes to give the heptaoxide and the dioxide.[50]

Rhenium trioxide has a simple cubic structure[47, 52] with $a = 3.734 \pm 0.006$ Å and the radius of the Re^{6+} ion was derived as 0.55 Å. There is one molecular unit per unit cell. The rhenium atom occupies a cubic corner and the oxygens are at the centres of the edges, forming an octahedron about each rhenium, each oxygen belonging to two octahedra.

The heat of formation of rhenium trioxide has been measured twice but in each case the errors and uncertainties in the measurements were large. Roth and Becker[7] obtained a value of -83.0 kcal/mole but their calculations were based upon heats observed when rhenium metal burned to give a mixture of large amounts of rhenium heptaoxide and small varying amounts (4–8%) of rhenium trioxide. The combustion of rhenium trioxide also gave an unavoidable error in calculating the heat of formation of the trioxide because the trioxide did not burn completely even in the presence of an oil accelerator and a correction had to be applied for the unreacted material. These experiments gave a value of -146 kcal/mole for the heat of formation.[8]

Between 325° and 420° the vapour pressure of rhenium trioxide, measured by the effusion method, was given by the equation[53]

$$\log p = \frac{-10.882}{T} + 15.16$$

The heat of sublimation was calculated to be 49.78 kcal/mole and the extrapolated boiling point was 614°.

Rhenium trioxide is slightly paramagnetic, a temperature-independent molar susceptibility of 68×10^{-6} e.m.u. has been observed.[54]

Technetium trioxide.—It is not certain whether technetium trioxide has ever been prepared, it has certainly never been well characterized. Fried and Hall[55] described a volatile purple oxide, $TcO_{3.05}$, from the reaction of oxygen on technetium metal at 400–1000° but later workers only obtained the pale yellow heptaoxide.[14]

More recently[56] a red solid thought to be technetium trioxide was obtained by the thermal decomposition of pertechnyl chloride, TcO_3Cl. The red solid reacted with chlorine to reform pertechnyl chloride—a reaction analogous to the behaviour of rhenium trioxide—but so far the solid has not been established definitely as technetium trioxide.

Rhenium dioxide.—Anhydrous rhenium dioxide has been prepared by the reduction of the heptaoxide with rhenium metal.[46]

$$2\, Re_2O_7 + 3\, Re \rightarrow 7\, ReO_2$$

Rhenium dioxide has also been prepared by reduction of the heptaoxide with hydrogen at 300°,[57] by the pyrolysis of ammonium perrhenate[58] and by the thermal dissociation of rhenium trioxide in a vacuum at 300°.[50] Hydrated rhenium dioxide may be dehydrated at 250° in a vacuum to give the anhydrous material.[59]

The hydrated dioxide $ReO_2 \cdot 2H_2O$ is readily prepared by the alkaline hydrolysis of the hexahalorhenate (IV) salts, M_2ReX^6, (where $X = Cl$, Br, I) but in this case the precipitated dioxide absorbs a large amount of cationic impurities.[60] A very pure form of the hydrated dioxide may be prepared by hydrolysing rhenium pentachloride in water.[59] Hydrated rhenium dioxide may be prepared by the action of various reducing agents on solutions of perrhenates. Thus Briscoe and coworkers[60] found that hydrazine, zinc and hydrochloric acid and also stannous chloride all reduced perrhenate solutions to give first of all yellow colloidal solutions of the dioxide from which black precipitates of the hydrated dioxide gradually separated out.

There appear to be two forms of rhenium dioxide. A monoclinic variety with the molybdenum dioxide type of structure, has been described.[61] The full details of this structure have not been worked out, but the unit cell dimensions are so similar to those of molybdenum and tungsten dioxides that it is likely that the atoms occupy similar positions in the rhenium dioxide lattice. The unit cell dimensions found are given in Table 3-7.

Table 3-7. Unit cell dimensions of the dioxides

	Rhenium dioxide[61] (monoclinic)	Rhenium dioxide[62] (orthorhombic)	Technetium dioxide[61]
a (Å)	5.562	4.8094	5.53
b (Å)	4.848	5,6433	4.79
c (Å)	5.561	4.6007	5.53
β	120°87′	—	120°

An orthorhombic form of rhenium dioxide has been prepared by annealing samples at high temperature.[62] The orthorhombic form is the stable form within the range 300–1500°. The unit cell dimensions are given in Table 3-7.

There were four formula units per unit all giving a theoretical density of 11.61 in good agreement with the value of 11.4 determined by Biltz.[46] By annealing rhenium dioxide at 1050° for several weeks single crystals were obtained suitable for x-ray work. The space group was shown to be Pbcn and the structure consisted of zig-zag chains of rhenium atoms parallel to the c axis with a metal–metal distance of 2.61 Å.

Rhenium dioxide is insoluble in water and aqueous alkalis, but it is readily attacked by oxidizing acids and alkaline hydrogen peroxide solutions to give the perrhenate ion. Fusion with alkalis in the absence of air gives the rhenites, $ReO_3{}^{2-}$. Rhenium dioxide dissolves in the halogen acids to give finally the hexahalorhenates (IV). It is reduced to the metal by hydrogen at 500° and heating in air or oxygen produces the heptaoxide.

The magnetic moment of rhenium dioxide is very low, indicating considerable metal–metal interaction. A molar susceptibility of 43.6×10^{-6} e.m.u. has been recorded for the anhydrous material.[63] The susceptibilities recorded for the hydrated dioxide were also very low ranging between 139×10^{-6} e.m.u. at 398° and 266×10^{-6} e.m.u. at 78°.[54]

The vapour pressure of rhenium dioxide between 650° and 785° follows the equation

$$\log p = \frac{-14{,}437}{T} + 11.65$$

giving a heat of sublimation of 65.64 kcal/mole and an estimated temperature of 1363° at which the vapour pressure rises to 760 mm.[53]

Technetium dioxide.—Technetium dioxide is similar to its rhenium analogue. The anhydrous material has been prepared by the thermal decomposition of ammonium pertechnetate[64] and by dehydrating the dihydrate in a vacuum at 300°.[54] Technetium dioxide dihydrate has been prepared by reducing pertechnetate solutions with zinc and hydrochloric acid. The dioxide was first formed as a colloidal solution which coagulated to a black solid on addition of a large excess of ammonia solution. Technetium dioxide has also probably been prepared by the electrolytic reduction of alkali pertechnetate solutions.[65] The black deposit was assumed to be the dioxide and not the metal because it dissolved in an ammonia–hydrogen peroxide mixture which does not dissolve technetium metal, however it is possible that the product was a lower oxide of technetium or very finely divided reactive metal.

Anhydrous technetium dioxide has the molybdenum dioxide structure,[61] the approximate unit cell dimensions are given in Table 3-7.

The magnetic susceptibility of technetium dioxide dihydrate is very low.[54] Although the susceptibility varies with temperature the Curie–Weiss Law is not obeyed and there must be considerable metal–metal interaction.

Anhydrous technetium dioxide is a very stable compound, it can be sublimed at about 1000° in a vacuum without decomposition.[54] The dioxide can be reduced to the metal by hydrogen at 500° and heating in oxygen gives the heptaoxide as with rhenium. It reacts with chlorine to give a mixture of oxide chlorides and with bromine to give technetium oxide tribromide.[56]

Lower rhenium oxides.—Rhenium sesquioxide $Re_2O_3 \cdot xH_2O$, has been isolated by the hydrolysis of rhenium trichloride by alkalis in the absence of air.[66] It was a black solid which was very readily oxidized to the hydrated dioxide. Nothing more is known of this oxide.

Young and Irvine[67] obtained some interesting results, concerning the oxides of univalent and divalent rhenium, which appear to have been neglected and remain unconfirmed. They found that perrhenic acid was reduced by zinc and hydrochloric acid over a period of days under a carbon dioxide atmosphere. The black insoluble precipitate appeared to be hydrated rhenium (I) oxide. The compound was partly soluble in hydrochloric acid without evolution of hydrogen (rhenium metal is insoluble in hydrochloric acid). The oxidation state of the rhenium in the compound was found to be one, water and oxygen were determined by reduction with hydrogen, a ratio of $Re:O = 2:3$ was obtained, suggesting that the formula of the compound was $Re_2O \cdot 2H_2O$.

Reduction of perrhenic acid with cadmium instead of zinc gave a different, rather inert oxide which was thought to be $ReO \cdot H_2O$. This oxide dissolved in nitric acid and bromine water and was slowly oxidized by air, but it was unaffected by hydrochloric acid or alkali solutions.

No oxides of technetium of oxidation state less than four have been reported.

Gaseous oxides of rhenium.—In a mass spectrometer study of rhenium surfaces treated with nitric acid the species listed in Table 3-8 were identified.[68]

Table 3-8. Gaseous rhenium oxides

Monomers	Dimers
Re^+	Re_2^+
ReO^+	Re_2O^+
ReO_2^+	$Re_2O_2^+$
ReO_3^+	$Re_2O_3^+$
ReO_4^+	$Re_2O_4^+$
	$Re_2O_5^+ \; Re_2O_5^{2+}$
	$Re_2O_6^+$
	$Re_2O_7^+ \; Re_2O_7^{2+}$

Since rhenium heptaoxide was the heaviest mass observed it must have been the primary gaseous product from the surface. ReO_4^+ species was also thought to be a primary gaseous product as it was sometimes observed in the absence of other oxides. It is of interest to note that the species

$ReO_3{}^+$ appears at masses 233 and 235 and it is possible it may interfere with uranium isotopic analyses when rhenium filaments are used.

Sulphur Compounds

Rhenium heptasulphide.—Rhenium heptasulphide may be prepared by passing hydrogen sulphide into potassium perrhenate solutions. In ammoniacal solutions a pink colour was first formed and black rhenium heptasulphide slowly precipitated out.[69] Miller and Lander[70] found the precipitation to be quantitative but very slow (24–48 hours). In acid solutions precipitation did not begin until the solution was saturated with hydrogen sulphide.[70]

No visible reaction occurred on warming sodium thiosulphate with potassium perrhenate solution, but on acidification of the solution sulphur and rhenium heptasulphide were precipitated.[69] The precipitation of rhenium was quantitative after prolonged boiling and the free sulphur was extracted with boiling toluene.

Rhenium heptasulphide is a black powder which is readily converted to the perrhenate ion by the action of alkaline hydrogen peroxide solution on nitric acid. On heating to about 450° in a vacuum it decomposes to rhenium disulphide.[71]

Rhenium heptasulphide precipitated from hydrochloric acid solutions has a tetragonal lattice with $a = 13.7 \pm 0.03$ Å and $c = 10.24 \pm 0.66$ Å.[72] Traore and coworkers[72] also claimed that the thermal decomposition of rhenium heptasulphide in a nitrogen atmosphere gave both rhenium disulphide and trisulphide and that the trisulphide was also formed by hydrogen reduction of rhenium heptasulphide at room temperature.

The heat of combustion of rhenium heptasulphide has been determined,[73] the combustion giving both sulphur dioxide and trioxide:

$$Re_2S_7(c) + \frac{21}{2} O_2(g) \rightarrow Re_2O_7(c) + 7 SO_2(g)$$

$$Re_2S_7(c) + 14 O_2(g) \rightarrow Re_2O_7(c) + 7 SO_3(s)$$

Experimentally the fraction of sulphur appearing as sulphur dioxide was 0.883 ± 0.019 and was independent of the amount of sulphide burnt. The average energy of combustion from the two equations was $- 1.1743 \pm 0.0019$ cal/mg Re_2S_7. After correcting to 100% sulphur trioxide, the heat of combustion of rhenium heptasulphide was calculated to be

$$\Delta H° = - 849.9 \pm 1.7 \text{ kcal/mole}$$

Using auxiliary thermochemical data the heat of formation of rhenium heptasulphide was calculated to be $- 107.9 \pm 1.8$ kcal/mole at 25°.

Rhenium heptaselenide was prepared by passing hydrogen selenide into potassium perrhenate solution. It was very similar to the heptasulphide and decomposed in a vacuum at about 330° to give rhenium diselenide.[69]

Technetium heptasulphide.—Technetium heptasulphide was precipitated by the action of hydrogen sulphide on a pertechnetate dissolved in 2–4 N hydrochloric acid.[74] The crude material contained a good deal of free sulphur which was removed with carbon disulphide.

Technetium heptasulphide closely resembles its rhenium analogue; it is readily converted to the pertechnetate ion by alkali hydrogen peroxide solutions and it is thermally decomposed to technetium disulphide in a vacuum on heating. It is reduced to technetium metal by hydrogen at 1100°.[75]

Rhenium disulphide.—Rhenium disulphide may be prepared either by the thermal decomposition of the heptasulphide in vacuum or by direct combination of the elements at red heat.[69, 71]

Rhenium disulphide is a dense black solid which is chemically rather inert. It has the molybdenum disulphide structure with $a = 3.14$ Å and $c = 12.20$ Å with a density of 7.5 gm/cc at 25°.[76]

The heat of formation of rhenium disulphide is $- 42.7 \pm 1.2$ kcal/mole at 25°.[73] Its vapour pressure is between 500° and 700° and is given by the equation

$$\log p = \frac{- 4976}{T} + 3.214$$

from which the heat of sublimation was found to be 22.66 kcal/mole.[53]

Rhenium diselenide is a black inert compound formed by the thermal decomposition of rhenium heptaselenide at 330° in a vacuum.[69]

Technetium disulphide.—Amorphous technetium disulphide is prepared by the thermal decomposition of the heptasulphide but a crystalline modification has been prepared by heating the heptasulphide with sulphur at 1000° for 24 hours.[77] It is isostructural with rhenium disulphide but lattice parameters are not available.

Chlorination of rhenium sulphides.—Chlorination of rhenium disulphide gave rhenium pentachloride and a non-volatile sulphidechloride $ReSCl_2$. By prolonged treatment with chlorine at 400–500° the sulphidechloride was completely converted to rhenium pentachloride.[78] The proposed reaction scheme was

$$ReS_2 \rightarrow ReSCl_2 \rightarrow [ReCl_4] \rightarrow ReCl_5$$

Subsequently it was thought that ReS_2Cl_2 may be an intermediate and in an attempt to isolate this compound the chlorination of rhenium heptasulphide was investigated.[79] To avoid exothermic chlorination of the heptasulphide the chlorine was diluted 1 : 5 with carbon dioxide and the chlorination was studied in the temperature range 20–180° in 20° steps. Below 120° a product remained in the furnace, but above 120° volatile rhenium pentachloride was the only product observed.

Analysis showed the intermediate to be $Re_2S_3Cl_4$. It was dark brown and amorphous to x-rays. It was soluble in water and alcohol, the aqueous solution being hydrolysed on boiling or by the addition of alkali.[79]

References

1. I. and W. NODDACK, Z. Anorg. Allgem. Chem. 181, 1 (1929).
2. H. V. A. BRISCOE, P. L. ROBINSON and A. J. RUDGE, Nature 129, 618 (1932).
3. A. D. MELAVEN, J. N. FOWLE, W. BRICKNELL and C. F. HISKEY, Inorganic Syntheses, Vol. III, 188.
4. K. WILHELM, Acta Chem. Scand. 8, 693 (1954).
5. E. OGAWA, Bull. Chem. Soc. Japan 7, 265 (1932).
6. W. T. SMITH, JNR., L. E. LINE, JNR. and W. A. BELL, J. Am. Chem. Soc. 74, 4965 (1954).
7. W. A. ROTH and G. BECKER, Z. Physik. Chem. A159, 27 (1932).
8. G. E. BOYD, J. W. COBBLE and W. T. SMITH, JNR., J. Am. Chem. Soc. 75, 5783 (1953).
9. R. H. BUSEY, J. Am. Chem. Soc. 78, 3263 (1956).
10. G. E. BOYD, J. W. COBBLE, C. M. NELSON and W. T. SMITH, JNR., J. Am. Chem. Soc. 74, 556 (1952).
11. R. D. ELLISON, quoted in reference 12.
12. W. T. SMITH, JNR., J. W. COBBLE and G. E. BOYD, J. Am. Chem. Soc. 75, 5773 (1953).
13. R. COLTON and R. D. PEACOCK, Quart. Rev. London 16, 299 (1962).
14. J. W. COBBLE, W. T. SMITH, JNR. and G. E. BOYD, J. Am. Chem. Soc. 75, 5777 (1953).
15. R. COLTON, J. DALZIEL, W. P. GRIFFITH and G. WILKINSON, J. Chem. Soc. 71 (1960).
16. A. A. WOOLF, Quart. Rev. London 15, 372 (1961).
17. N. BAILEY, A. CARRINGTON, K. A. KHOTT and M. C. R. SYMONS, J. Chem. Soc. 290 (1960).
18. R. COLTON, U.K.A.E.A. Document A.E.R.E.-R3823 (1961).
19. A. S. KERTES and A. BECK, J. Chem. Soc. 1926 (1961).
20. J. BEINTEMA, Zeit. Krist. 97, 300 (1937).
21. L. H. AHRENS, Geochim. Cosmochim. Acta 2, 155 (1952).
22. H. H. CLAASSEN and A. J. ZIELEN, J. Chem. Phys. 22, 707 (1954).
23. R. FONTEYNE, Natuurw. Tijdschr. Ghent 20, 20 (1938).
24. C. G. BARRACLOUGH, J. LEWIS and R. S. NYHOLM, J. Chem. Soc. 3552 (1959).
25. W. T. SMITH, JNR. and S. H. LONG, J. Am. Chem. Soc. 70, 354 (1948).
26. J. H. JONES, J. Am. Chem. Soc. 68, 240 (1946).
27. J. W. COBBLE, G. D. OLIVER and W. T. SMITH, JNR., J. Am. Chem. Soc. 75, 5786 (1953).
28. W. T. SMITH, JNR. and G. E. MAXWELL, J. Am. Chem. Soc. 73, 658 (1951).
29. W. T. SMITH, JNR., J. Am. Chem. Soc. 73, 77 (1951).

30. W. T. SMITH, JNR. and G. E. MAXWELL, *J. Am. Chem. Soc.* **71**, 578 (1949).
31. E. WILKE-DORFURT and T. GUNZERT, *Z. Anorg. Allgem. Chem.* **215**, 369 (1933).
32. M. SCHMIDT and H. SCHNIDBAUR, *Chem. Ber.* **92**, 2667 (1959).
33. B. SCHARNOW, *Z. Anorg. Allgem. Chem.* **215**, 185 (1933).
34. A. W. SLEIGHT and R. WARD, *J. Am. Chem. Soc.* **83**, 1088 (1961).
35. W. FEIT, *Z. Anorg. Allgem. Chem.* **199**, 262 (1931).
36. H. V. A. BRISCOE, P. L. ROBINSON and E. M. STODDART, *J. Chem. Soc.* 2976 (1931).
37. H. V. A. BRISCOE, P. L. ROBINSON and E. M. STODDART, *J. Chem. Soc.* 2811 (1932).
38. G. H. CARTLEDGE and W. T. SMITH, JNR. *J. Phys. Chem.* **59**, 1111 (1955).
39. G. E. BOYD, *J. Chem. Educ.* **36**, 3 (1959).
40. R. H. BUSEY and R. BEVAN, *Unclassified Document* O.R.N.L. 2983 (1960).
41. R. H. BUSEY and Q. V. LARSON, *Unclassified Document* O.R.N.L. 2584 (1958).
42. A. J. MCDONALD and G. J. TYSON, *Acta. Cryst.* **15**, 87 (1962).
43. K. SCHWOCHAU, *Zeit. Naturforsch.* **174**, 630 (1962).
44. J. W. COBBLE, C. M. NELSON, G. W. PARKER, W. T. SMITH, JNR. and G. E. BOYD, *J. Am. Chem. Soc.* **74**, 1852 (1952).
45. G. H. CARTLEDGE, *Corrosion* **11**, 355 (1955).
46. W. BILTZ, *Z. Anorg. Allgem. Chem.* **214**, 225 (1933).
47. W. BILTZ, G. A. LAHNAR and K. MEISEL, *Nachr. Akad. Wiss. Goettingen Math. Physik. Kl.* **191** (1931).
48. H. V. A. BRISCOE, P. L. ROBINSON and A. J. RUDGE, *J. Chem. Soc.* 3087 (1931).
49. H. NECHAMKIN and C. F. HISKEY, *Inorganic Syntheses* Vol. III, 186 (1950).
50. H. NECHAMKIN, A. N. KURTZ and C. F. HISKEY, *J. Am. Chem. Soc.* **73**, 2829 (1951).
51. A. D. MELAVEN, J. N. FOWLE, W. BRICKELL and C. F. HISKEY, *Inorganic Syntheses* Vol. III, 187 (1950).
52. K. MEISEL, *Z. Anorg. Allgem. Chem.* **207**, 121 (1932).
53. V. I. DEEV and V. I. SMIRNOV, *Dokl. Akad. Nauk. SSSR* **140**, 822 (1961).
54. C. M. NELSON, G. E. BOYD and W. T. SMITH, JNR., *J. Am. Chem. Soc.* **76**, 348 (1954).
55. S. FRIED and N. F. HALL, *Phys. Rev.* **81**, 741 (1951).
56. R. COLTON, unpublished work.
57. I. and W. NODDACK, *Z. Anorg. Allgem. Chem.* **181**, 32 (1929).
58. W. FREUNLICH and A. DESCHANURES, *Compt. Rend.* **245**, 1809 (1957).
59. H. V. A. BRISCOE, P. L. ROBINSON and E. M. STODDART, *J. Chem. Soc.* 666 (1931).
60. D. BROWN and R. COLTON, *Nature* **198**, 1300 (1963).
61. W. H. ZACHARIASEN quoted by A. MAGNELI and G. ANDERSSON, *Acta Chem. Scand.* **9**, 1378 (1955).
62. A. MAGNELI, *Acta Chem. Scand.* **11**, 28 (1957).
63. W. SCHUH and W. KLEMM, *Z. Anorg. Allgem. Chem.* **220**, 193 (1934).
64. S. FRIED and N. F. HALL, *Chemistry of Technetium* Am. Chem. Soc. Meeting (1950).
65. L. B. ROGERS, *J. Am. Chem. Soc.* **71**, 1507 (1949).
66. W. GEILMANN, F. W. WRIGGE and W. BILTZ, *Z. Anorg. Allgem. Chem.* **214**, 239 (1950).

67. R. C. Young and J. W. Irvine, Jnr., *J. Am. Chem. Soc.* **59**, 2648 (1937).
68. M. H. Studier, *J. Phys. Chem.* **66**, 189 (1962).
69. H. V. A. Briscoe, P. L. Robinson and E. M. Stoddart, *J. Chem. Soc.* 1439 (1931).
70. J. H. Miller and W. H. Lander, *J. Am. Chem. Soc.* **2376** (1933).
71. W. Biltz and F. Weibke, *Z. Anorg. Allgem. Chem.* **203**, 3 (1931).
72. K. Traore, G. Coeffier and J. P. Brenet, *Bull. Soc. Chim. France* **361** (1962).
73. J. E. McDonald and J. W. Cobble, *J. Phys. Chem.* **66**, 791 (1962).
74. C. L. Rulfs and W. W. Meinke, *J. Am. Chem. Soc.* **74**, 235 (1952).
75. S. Fried, *J. Am. Chem. Soc.* **70**, 442 (1948).
76. K. Meisel, *Z. Angew. Chem.* **44**, 243 (1931).
77. W. H. Zachariasen, quoted in reference 39.
78. V. G. Tronev, G. A. Bekhtle and S. B. Davidyants, *Trudy Akad. Nauk Tadzhik SSR* **84**, 105 (1958).
79. I. A. Glukhov, S. B. Davidyants, M. A. Yanusov and N. A. El'manova, *Zh. Neorgan. Khim.* **6**, 1264 (1961).

4

Halides and Oxide Halides

In common with many other transition metals there has been a remarkable upsurge in interest and research in the simple halides and oxide halides of rhenium in the last few years. No less than ten simple binary halides of rhenium have been prepared for the first time in the last five years. Recently the halide chemistry of technetium has been studied but so far comparatively few compounds have been prepared.

Rhenium–fluorine chemistry is extensive even though there are no compounds in which the oxidation number of the metal is less than four. Recent work has produced a number of new compounds including the unique heptafluoride. Rhenium is remarkable in that it has four binary fluorides ranging from the tetrafluoride to the heptafluoride. In addition there are at least six oxide fluorides and several types of complex fluorides.

Until recently only two binary chlorides of rhenium were known; the brown pentachloride was thought to be the only product of the action of chlorine on the metal and it had been known for many years that this could be thermally decomposed in a stream of nitrogen to give the involatile trichloride. Technetium on the other hand was known to give only the tetrachloride by the interaction of the heptaoxide and carbon tetrachloride in a sealed tube. An investigation of the interaction of the metal and chlorine led to the characterization of technetium hexachloride. Thus the unusual situation arose of the second-row transition metal showing a higher covalency in its chlorides than the corresponding third-row element and it was suggested that rhenium hexachloride should exist. A further study of the rhenium–chlorine reaction in fact led to the characterization of the hexachloride. Rhenium tetrachloride has also been prepared and it is quite different to the stable technetium compound, rather it resembles rhenium tetrabromide and tetraiodide.

The bromides of rhenium have scarcely been studied at all. Two new binary compounds and two oxide bromides have been characterized recently and they show that the rhenium–bromine system very closely resembles the rhenium–chlorine system. An oxide bromide of technetium has been characterized but no binary compounds are known.

A remarkable series of iodides from rhenium moniodide to rhenium tetraiodide is known but no corresponding technetium compounds have yet been reported.

The alkaline hydrolysis of all halides and complex halides of both rhenium and technetium follows a well defined pattern. A compound of Re^{VII} always hydrolyses to perrhenate and no precipitate appears. Compounds of Re^{VI} and Re^V always disproportionate into Re^{IV} and Re^{VII}. The fraction appearing as Re^{IV} is always obtained as the insoluble hydrated dioxide which can be separated from the soluble perrhenate. Compounds of Re^{IV} hydrolyse to give all the rhenium as the dioxide. These reactions are summarized in the following equations

$$Re^{VII} \xrightarrow{\text{alkali}} \underset{\text{(soluble)}}{Re^{VII}}$$

$$3\ Re^{VI} \xrightarrow{\text{alkali}} \underset{\text{(soluble)}}{2\ Re^{VII}} + \underset{\text{(insoluble)}}{Re^{IV}}$$

$$3\ Re^V \xrightarrow{\text{alkali}} \underset{\text{(soluble)}}{Re^{VII}} + \underset{\text{(insoluble)}}{2\ Re^{IV}}$$

$$Re^{IV} \xrightarrow{\text{alkali}} \underset{\text{(insoluble)}}{Re^{IV}}$$

This type of behaviour is of very wide application and will be referred to repeatedly in the following pages. It is very useful to help in characterizing new compounds, especially of technetium. The only compounds of all the halides, oxide halides or complex halides of rhenium or technetium (IV), (V), (VI) or (VII) which do not obey these rules are rhenium and technetium tetrachlorides. These compounds do not hydrolyse at all easily probably because they are polymeric in nature.

Rhenium Fluorides

Rhenium heptafluoride.—It has recently been shown that rhenium heptafluoride is formed by the action of fluorine at 250 mm pressure on rhenium metal at 300–400°.[1, 2] The reaction product is always a mixture of the hepta-fluoride and the hexafluoride, the actual proportions depending on the experimental conditions. Low temperatures favour the formation of the hexafluoride. As it was found to be almost impossible to separate the two fluorides, the mixture was heated with fluorine at 3 atmospheres pressure at 400° for several hours. Under these conditions the hexafluoride is quantitatively converted to the heptafluoride.

Rhenium heptafluoride is a yellow solid very similar in appearance to the hexafluoride, a fact which no doubt delayed its discovery. Malm and Selig studied the physical properties of both rhenium heptafluoride and hexafluoride and have shown quite conclusively that almost all the earlier samples of the hexafluoride were in fact contaminated with the higher fluoride.[2]

Rhenium heptafluoride is stable and can be kept indefinitely in dry pyrex glass. It is thermally stable but instantly hydrolysed by water to give perrhenic and hydrofluoric acids. It is reduced by rhenium metal to the hexafluoride but rather remarkably it does not react with oxygen even when heated to 500° for several hours.

The vapour pressure of rhenium heptafluoride has been measured over a fairly wide temperature range.[1, 2] The following equations were deduced from the experimental data

solid ReF_7 $(- 14.47°$ to $48.3°)$

$$\log_{10}p = - \frac{2205.8}{T} - 1.4703 \log_{10}T + 13.04321$$

liquid ReF_7 $(48.3°$ to $74.61°)$

$$\log_{10}p = - \frac{244.28}{T} + 9.90825 \log_{10}T - 21.58352$$

From these data various thermodynamic properties have been calculated and these are shown in Table 4-1 together with those of the hexafluoride. The infra-red spectrum of rhenium heptafluoride is shown in Fig. 1 and is discussed below together with that of the hexafluoride.

Rhenium hexafluoride.—Rhenium hexafluoride is always formed to-gether with the heptafluoride when fluorine reacts with heated rhenium metal. It was first investigated by Ruff and coworkers[3, 4, 5] although Malm and Selig[2] suggest that Ruff's material contained much heptafluoride judging by its vapour pressure. The best way to obtain the hexafluoride is to heat the reaction mixture from the fluorine and rhenium reaction with

E

excess of rhenium metal. Under these conditions the heptafluoride is quantitatively reduced to the hexafluoride.[2]

Rhenium hexafluoride is a yellow solid which melts at 18.5°. It is very reactive towards water, giving the usual disproportionation reaction for Re^{VI} compounds.

$$3 \, Re^{VI} \rightarrow 2 \, Re^{VII} + Re^{IV}$$

In contrast to the early reports of Ruff and coworkers, later investigators have found that rhenium hexafluoride does not attack glass or silica. Malm and Selig[2] find that, like the heptafluoride, it does not react with oxygen at 500°. This behaviour is in contrast to that of the binary compounds of rhenium with the other halogens which all react very readily with oxygen. It is interesting to note that Ruff and Kwasnik[5] claimed to have prepared rhenium oxide tetrafluoride, $ReOF_4$, and rhenium dioxide difluoride, ReO_2F_2, by the action of oxygen on the hexafluoride. Later workers have since made these compounds and they are quite different from Ruff's products. Rhenium hexafluoride can also be made by the action of chlorine trifluoride gas on rhenium metal at 300°.[6] The mixture of chlorine trifluoride and rhenium hexafluoride collected in a cooled trap was dissolved in hydrofluoric acid and the solution cooled in dry ice. Large yellow crystals of an adduct $ReF_6 \cdot xClF_3$ were obtained which were decomposed by distilling in a platinum tube at 50° under hydrogen. The rhenium hexafluoride was purified by pumping at $-70°$ for 4 hours. Its melting point was 18.7° agreeing with the values given below.

The vapour pressure of rhenium hexafluoride has recently been measured by Malm and Selig[2] and by Cady and Hargreaves.[7] The vapour pressures obtained by the two groups agreed quite well and the equations deduced from the experimental data are

Solid $(-50°$ to $-1.9°)$ $\qquad \log_{10}p = 10.110 - \dfrac{2151.2}{T}$

(Cady and Hargreaves)

Solid I $(-10.47$ to $-3.45°)$ $\log_{10}p = -\dfrac{2303.6}{T} - 0.8327 \log_{10}T$

(Malm and Selig) $\hfill + 12.70721$

Solid II $(-3.45°$ to $18.5°)$ $\quad \log_{10}p = -\dfrac{1765.4}{T} - 0.1790 \log_{10}7$

$\hfill + 9.12298$

Liquid ReF_6 (18.5 to 48.06°) $\log_{10}p = -\dfrac{1956.7}{7} - 3.599 \log_{10}T$

$\hfill + 18.20814$

Thermodynamic data have been calculated from the vapour pressure measurements and these are shown in Table 4-1 together with those for rhenium heptafluoride.

The solid–solid transition for rhenium hexafluoride was observed by both groups of workers and Malm and Selig confirmed the change by x-ray diffraction studies.[2] They found that the high temperature phase ($-3.54°$ to $18.5°$) has a body-centred cubic structure isostructural with

Table 4-1. Thermodynamic properties of ReF_7 and ReF_6

	ReF_7	ReF_6 Malm and Selig	ReF_6 Cady and Hargreaves
Triple point °c	48.3	18.5	18.7
Boiling point °c	73.72	33.68	33.8
Liquid density g/c.c	3.65 ± 0.02 (52°)	3.58 ± 0.02 (22°)	—
Solid–solid trans. °c	—	− 3.45	− 1.9
Heat of transition cal/mole	—	2027	2090
Entropy of trans. cal/mole/deg	—	7.52	7.71
Heat of fusion cal/mole	1799	1107	940
Entropy of fusion cal/mole/deg	5.60	3.80	3.21
Heat of vapour cal/mole	9154 (48.3°)	6867 (18.5°)	—

other metal hexafluorides. The low temperature form is again like the low temperature form of other metal hexafluorides but its symmetry is unknown.

The infra-red spectra of rhenium heptafluoride and hexafluoride provide a sensitive way of detecting an impurity of one in the other. Both spectra show a strong fundamental at 716 cm^{-1} attributed to the metal–fluorine bond but the heptafluoride shows additional peaks. The spectrum in the range 600–1600 cm^{-1} is shown in Fig. 1.

The infra-red spectrum obtained by Gaunt[8] for rhenium hexafluoride shows quite clearly that his sample contained some rhenium heptafluoride, but this does not affect his conclusion that the molecule is a perfect octahedron.

The infra-red and Raman spectra of rhenium hexafluoride rigorously purified from the heptafluoride has been obtained.[9] The fundamentals were assigned as follows

$$\nu_1 \quad \nu_2 \quad \nu_3 \quad \nu_4 \quad \nu_5 \quad \nu_6$$
$$755 \quad 596 \quad 715 \quad 257 \quad 246 \quad 193?$$

Octahedral symmetry. Point Group O_h

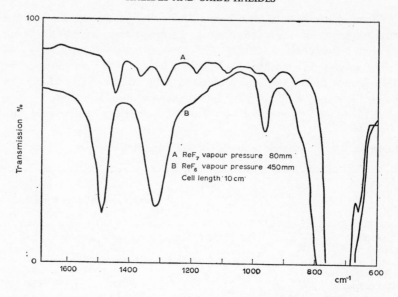

Figure 1. Infra-red spectra of rhenium heptafluoride and rhenium hexafluoride. (Reproduced from J. G. Malm and H. Selig, *J. Inorg. Nucl. Chem.* **20**, 189 (1961))

The magnetic properties of rhenium hexafluoride have been measured over the temperature range 14°–296°K, the molar susceptibility is given by

$$X_\mathrm{M}ReF_6 = (78 \pm 1 \times 10^{-4})/T + (0.87 \pm 0.03)10^{-4}$$

from which $\mu = 0.25$ B.M.[10] This low moment is attributed to spin-orbit coupling.

Rhenium pentafluoride.—In an unsuccessful attempt to prepare rhenium carbonyl fluoride, Hargreaves and Peacock[11] isolated rhenium pentafluoride, rhenium tetrafluoride and rhenium oxide tetrafluoride. The experimental conditions and the products formed are tabulated below.

Table 4-2. Reaction of rhenium hexafluoride with carbonyls

Reactants	Products
$ReF_6 + Re_2(CO)_{10}$	$ReOF_4$ + residue
ReF_6 (large excess) + $W(CO)_6$	$ReOF_4$, WF_6 + impure ReF_4
ReF_6 (small excess) + $W(CO)_6$	$ReOF_4$, ReF_5, WF_6 + impure ReF_4
ReF_6 (small excess) WF_6 (large excess) + $W(CO)_6$	ReF_5 + impure ReF_4

Rhenium pentafluoride is a green or yellow-green solid which melts at 48° to a yellow viscous oil which crystallizes with difficulty on cooling. It boils at 240° and at this temperature it undergoes an apparently irreversible disproportionation to the hexafluoride and tetrafluoride. Rhenium pentafluoride is decomposed by moist air and it is attacked violently by water according to the equation

$$3 \, ReF_5 + 6 \, H_2O \rightarrow ReF_6{}^{2-} + ReO_4{}^- + ReO_2 + 9 \, F^- + 12 \, H^+$$

The magnetic susceptibility of rhenium pentafluoride has been measured over a wide temperature range[11] and the results are shown in Table 4-3. The detailed interpretation of this data is difficult because the structure of the solid is unknown, but it is possible that a polymeric structure with metal–metal bonds can explain the data.

Table 4-3. Magnetic properties of rhenium pentafluoride

Temp. (°K)	$\chi_M \times 10^6$	μ(B.M.)
295.0	835	1.41
272.0	864	1.38
249.0	887	1.33
231.0	905	1.30
210.0	940	1.26
191.0	952	1.21
170.0	971	1.15
149.5	996	1.09
129.5	1024	1.01
110.5	1049	0.97
105.0	1067	0.95
	$\theta = 580°$	

The vapour pressure of rhenium pentafluoride has been measured.[12] The equation deduced from the experimental data is

$$\log_{10}p = 9.024 - \frac{3037}{T} \; (48.0° \text{ to } 140°)$$

Certain thermodynamic properties have been calculated and they are given below.

Triple point	48°
Boiling point	221.3°
Heat of vaporization	13,880 cal/mole
Entropy of vaporization	28.1 cal/mole/deg

Rhenium tetrafluoride.—Ruff[3, 4, 5] claimed to have prepared rhenium tetrafluoride by reduction of the hexafluoride with hydrogen at 200°, with carbon monoxide at 300° and with sulphur dioxide at 400°. The properties of this material however are not the same as those described by Hargreaves and Peacock[11] and these authors suggest that Ruff obtained a mixture of the pentafluoride and the tetrafluoride.

Rhenium tetrafluoride is best obtained as a pale blue powdery residue from the thermal decomposition of rhenium pentafluoride. It is not very volatile but it can be sublimed without decomposition at about 300° in a vacuum. It is hydrolysed by water giving rhenium dioxide and hydrofluoric acid. Nothing is known of the structure of rhenium tetrafluoride as it was not possible to index the powder photographs.[11]

No lower fluorides of rhenium are known. Emeleus and Gutman[13] reacted rhenium trichloride with hydrofluoric acid, at 240° an intermediate was observed but only rhenium trichloride and rhenium metal were isolated from the mixture. At 350° the only products were rhenium metal and a trace of rhenium hexafluoride. These workers suggested that a lower fluoride was formed and that it undergoes spontaneous decomposition.

$$ReCl_3 + HF \rightleftharpoons ReF_3 + 3HCl$$

$$ReF_3 \rightarrow Re + \frac{3}{2} F_2$$

Rhenium Oxide Fluorides

Ruff and Kwasnik claimed to have prepared rhenium oxide tetrafluoride $ReOF_4$ and rhenium dioxide difluoride ReO_2F_2 by passing a mixture of fluorine and oxygen over heated rhenium metal, but this appears to be incorrect especially as both were described as colourless. These compounds could not be confirmed by Robinson and coworkers who isolated instead rhenium oxide pentafluoride $ReOF_5$ and rhenium dioxide trifluoride ReO_2F_3. The other possible heptavalent oxide fluoride ReO_3F has also been prepared and these three compounds form a well-defined series. The genuine rhenium oxide tetrafluoride has since been obtained as a blue solid and yet another compound, rhenium oxide trifluoride can be obtained from it.

Rhenium oxide pentafluoride.—Rhenium oxide pentafluoride $ReOF_5$, is one of the products formed by the reaction of fluorine on potassium perrhenate heated to about 100°.[14] Once reaction has begun the potassium perrhenate melts with the heat evolved. The other product of the reaction is rhenium dioxide trifluoride ReO_2F_3 and the ratio of the amounts of the products is usually $ReOF_5 : ReO_2F_3 = 1:10$. The action of fluorine on rhenium dioxide gives the same products but usually the yields are in the ratio $ReOF_5 : ReO_2F_3 = 1 : 3$.

At room temperature rhenium oxide pentafluoride is a cream crystalline solid. It melts at 34.5° to a colourless liquid which boils at 55°/760 mm. In the absence of moisture the compound does not etch glass. It gives white fumes in moist air and it is instantly hydrolysed by water giving perrhenic and hydrofluoric acids.

$$ReOF_5 + 3\,H_2O \rightarrow HReO_4 + 5\,HF$$

This reaction confirms that the compound contains heptavalent rhenium since other oxidation states give precipitates of rhenium dioxide on hydrolysis.

The vapour pressure of rhenium oxide pentafluoride has been measured over a wide range of temperature.[12] There is a solid–solid transition at 30°, the vapour pressure equations deduced from the experimental data are as follows

Solid ReOF$_5$　　(0 to 30°) $\log_{10}p = 9.581 - \dfrac{2250}{T}$

Solid ReOF$_5$　(30° to 41°) $\log_{10}p = 8.620 - \dfrac{1958.9}{T}$

Liquid ReOF$_5$ (41° to 73°) $\log_{10}p = 7.727 - \dfrac{1678.6}{T}$

Some thermodynamic properties of rhenium oxide pentafluoride are given in Table 4-4.

Table 4-4. Thermodynamic properties of rhenium oxide pentafluoride

Triple point	40.8°
Boiling point	73.0°
Transition point	30.0°
Heat of transition	1339 cal/mole
Entropy of transition	3,868 cal/mole/deg
Heat of vaporization	7720 cal/mole
Entropy of vaporization	22.3 cal/mole/deg
Heat of sublimation (above 30°)	8940 cal/mole
Heat of sublimation (below 30°)	10,280 cal/mole

Rhenium dioxide trifluoride.—This is the second product resulting from the action of fluorine on potassium perrhenate or rhenium dioxide.[14] Rhenium dioxide trifluoride is a pale yellow solid which melts at 90°. The liquid solidifies to a glass but the compound may be obtained in a crystalline form by slow vacuum sublimation. Rhenium dioxide trifluoride does not attack glass up to 300°; it is easily hydrolysed by water to perrhenic and hydrofluoric acids.

The vapour pressure of rhenium dioxide trifluoride has been measured only for the liquid.[12] The vapour pressure equation (90°–170°) is

$$\log_{10} p = 10.36 - \frac{3437}{T}$$

Cady and Hargreaves[12] found the triple point to be 90° and estimated the boiling point as 185.4°. The heat and entropy of vaporization were calculated to be 15,700 cal/mole and 34.3 cal/mole/deg respectively.

Rhenium trioxide fluoride (perrhenyl fluoride).—The existence of perrhenyl fluoride was suspected by Ruff but he did not isolate the compound. It was first prepared by the interaction of perrhenyl chloride, ReO_3Cl, and anhydrous hydrofluoric acid.[15] The excess hydrofluoric acid was pumped away and the product was purified by vacuum sublimation.

Perrhenyl fluoride can also be prepared in good yield by the reaction of iodine pentafluoride on finely divided potassium perrhenate.[16] Reaction was only slight at room temperature, but on refluxing the potassium perrhenate dissolved to give a deep yellow solution, from which a yellow solid separated out on cooling. The excess iodine pentafluoride was pumped off and the product purified by vacuum sublimation at 140°.

Perrhenyl fluoride is a yellow solid melting at 147° to a very viscous yellow liquid which boils at 164° with slight decomposition.[15] The liquid usually solidifies to a glass but the compound can be obtained in a crystalline form by slow vacuum sublimation. Like the other heptavalent rhenium fluorides, perrhenyl fluoride does not attack glass, but it is very reactive towards moisture. It fumes in moist air and in water it is instantly hydrolysed to produce perrhenic and hydrofluoric acids.

The microwave spectrum of perrhenyl fluoride has been observed[17] and the molecule was found to be a symmetrical top like perrhenyl chloride. The following parameters were obtained

$$Re\text{–}O = 1.692 \pm 0.003 \text{ Å}$$
$$Re\text{–}F = 1.859 \pm 0.008 \text{ Å}$$
$$F\text{–}Re\text{–}O = 109° 31' \pm 16'$$

The dipole moment was found to be 0.85 ± 0.05 D.

The simple properties of the heptavalent rhenium fluorine compounds are given in Table 4-5 for reference.

Rhenium oxide tetrafluoride.—The preparation of rhenium oxide tetrafluoride $ReOF_4$ had been claimed by Ruff who described it as a colourless compound, but this claim can no longer be sustained in the light of present knowledge.

Table 4-5. Properties of heptavalent fluorine compounds

	Colour	M.p. (°c)	B.p. (°c)
ReF_7	yellow	48.3	73.72
$ReOF_5$	cream	35	55
ReO_2F_3	pale yellow	95	126
ReO_3F	yellow	147	164

Rhenium oxide tetrafluoride is one of the major products of the reaction of rhenium hexafluoride and metal carbonyls[11] as noted in the sections on rhenium pentafluoride and tetrafluoride. It is a blue crystalline solid which melts at 108° to a blue liquid, at 171° under atmospheric pressure it boils to give a colourless vapour. At 250° the vapour attacks pyrex glass to give a non-volatile product which is rhenium oxide trifluoride, $ReOF_3$. With water, rhenium oxide tetrafluoride behaves in the same way as rhenium hexafluoride, forming perrhenic and hydrofluoric acids and rhenium dioxide. The magnetic moment of the compound is roughly as expected for a Re^{VI} compound, it is lower than the spin only value and varies with temperature in a way somewhat similar to that predicted for an octachedral complex by Kotani.[18] The results are tabulated below in Table 4-6.

Table 4-6. Properties of rhenium oxide tetrafluoride

Temp. (°K)	$\chi_M \times 10^6$	μ (B.M.)
294.6	748.5	1.33
270.0	807.7	1.32
250.0	873.5	1.31
222.0	948.5	1.29
198.0	1047	1.29
175.0	1166	1.28
152.0	1303	1.26
130.0	1480	1.24
106.4	1762	1.23
84.1	2170	1.21
	$\theta = 34°$	

The vapour pressure of rhenium oxide tetrafluoride has been measured[12] and the equations deduced from the experimental data are

$$\text{solid } ReOF_4 \quad (50° \text{ to } 107°) \quad \log_{10} p = 11.88 - \frac{3888}{T}$$

$$\text{liquid } ReOF_4 \ (108° \text{ to } 172°) \quad \log_{10} p = 10.09 - \frac{3206}{T}$$

The following thermodynamic values were calculated

heat of vaporization   14,590 cal/mole
entropy of vaporization   32.7 cal/mole/deg
heat of sublimation   17,820 cal/mole

Rhenium oxide trifluoride.—Pyrex glass is slowly attacked at 250° by rhenium oxide tetrafluoride to give a black non-volatile compound which is rhenium oxide trifluoride, $ReOF_3$.[11] The compound has a tetragonal unit cell in which $a = 8.54$ and $c = 8.21$ Å. It is very hygroscopic and gives a blue aqueous solution which presumably contains a complex oxide fluoride ion.

Technetium Fluorides

Technetium hexafluoride.—Technetium hexafluoride has been prepared by the action of fluorine on technetium metal.[19] The metal, prepared by hydrogen reduction of ammonium pertechnetate at 600°, was reacted with excess fluorine in a nickel reactor for 2 hours at 400°. The volatile product was purified by fractional sublimation. The product was characterized as technetium hexafluoride in several ways and there was no evidence of formation of the heptafluoride. Measurement of the fluorine consumption during the reaction showed that 3 moles of fluorine were used for every mole of technetium. Vapour density determinations gave molecular weights which agreed with that required for the hexafluoride, chemical analysis gave an empirical formula of $TcF_{5.8}$.

Technetium hexafluoride is a golden yellow solid at room temperature, it melts to a yellow liquid at 37.4°,[20] the boiling point has been calculated to be 55.3° and the vapour is colourless and monomeric.[19] As with other transition metal hexafluorides there is a phase transition in the solid marking the change from the cubic high-temperature form to the orthorhombic low-temperature form; with technetium hexafluoride this change occurs at $-4.54°$ as calculated from vapour pressure data although it was actually observed at $-5.3°$.[20]

The vapour pressure of technetium hexafluoride has been measured over a temperature range and the following equations describe the results[20]

Solid I (-16.32 to $-5.3°$)

$$\log_{10}p = \frac{-3564.8}{T} - 10.787 \log_{10}T + 41.1252$$

Solid II (-5.3 to $37.4°$)

$$\log_{10}p = \frac{-2178.0}{T} - 2.295 \log_{10}T + 15.33427$$

Liquid (37.4 to 51.67°)

$$\log_{10}p = \frac{-2404.9}{T} - 5.8036 \log_{10}T + 24.8087$$

Thermodynamic data was calculated from the vapour pressure measurements and are recorded in Table 4-7.

Table 4-7. Thermodynamic data for technetium hexafluoride

Heat of sublimation	(solid II 37.4°)	8,555 cal/mole
Heat of sublimation	(solid I − 5.3°)	10,577 cal/mole
Heat of sublimation	(solid II − 5.3°)	8,750 cal/mole
Heat of vaporization	(solid II 37.4°)	7,427 cal/mole
Heat of fusion	(solid II 37.4°)	1,128 cal/mole
Entropy of fusion	(solid II 37.4°)	3.63 cal/mole/deg
Heat of transition		1,827 cal/mole
Entropy of transition		6.82 cal/mole/deg
Trouton constant (liquid)		22.0 cal/mole/deg

The infra-red spectrum of technetium hexafluoride shows only two sharp bands, the others are either missing or are broad.[21] A similar situation occurs for rhenium and tungsten hexafluorides and suggests that like these compounds technetium hexafluorides has O_h symmetry. The following assignments were made:

$$\begin{array}{cccccc} \nu_1 & \nu_2 & \nu_3 & \nu_4 & \nu_5 & \nu_6 \\ 705 & 551 & 748 & 265 & 255 & ? \text{ cm}^{-1} \end{array}$$

The magnetic moment of technetium hexafluoride is very low (0.45 B.M. at 300°K) and peculiar behaviour is observed below 14°K.[22]

Technetium pentafluoride.—It has recently been reported that technetium pentafluoride is a by-product of the fluorination of technetium metal.[23] Technetium pentafluoride is a yellow solid (m.p. 50°), it has an orthorhombic lattice ($a = 7.6$; $b = 5.8$; $c = 16.6$ Å) isostructural with that of chromium pentafluoride. It is more stable than rhenium pentafluoride although it begins to decompose at 60° in glass.

Technetium Oxide Fluorides

Technetium trioxide fluoride (pertechnyl fluoride).—The existence of pertechnyl fluoride, TcO_3F, was suspected some years ago from a mass-spectroscopic examination of the products formed from technetium heptaoxide and uranium tetrafluoride.[24]

Pertechnyl fluoride has since been isolated by passing fluorine over heated technetium dioxide.[25] It is surprising that a molecule containing three oxygen atoms per technetium should be obtained from a material containing only two oxygen atoms per technetium. Obviously some type of disproportionation reaction must occur giving an oxygen-deficient product as well as pertechnyl chloride. It was in fact reported that a gray residue remained in the reaction vessel but this was not identified. The difference between this reaction and that between fluorine and rhenium dioxide is also noteworthy, in this case rhenium dioxide trifluoride and rhenium oxide pentafluoride are the products.[14]

Pertechnyl fluoride is a yellow crystalline compound which melts at 18.3° to a yellow liquid. The boiling point, extrapolated from vapour pressure measurements is about 100°. It is stable at room temperature in nickel or monel but it attacks pyrex glassware. Water causes hydrolysis to pertechnic acid and hydrofluoric acids. Excess of fluorine at 400° and 4 atmospheres pressure gives technetium hexafluoride.[25]

The vapour pressure of pertechnyl fluoride is given by the following equations

solid ($- 8.78°$ to $18.28°$)

$$\log_{10}p = 12.448 \frac{- 3239.4}{T}$$

liquid (18.28 to $51.82°$)

$$\log_{10}p = 8.417 \frac{- 2064.6}{T}$$

Thermodynamic data have been calculated[25] and are given in Table 4-8.

Table 4-8. Thermodynamic data for pertechnyl fluoride

Melting point	18.3°
Boiling point	about 100°
Heat of sublimation	14.83 cal/mole
Heat of vaporization	9453 cal/mole
Heat of fusion	5377 cal/mole

Technetium oxide tetrafluoride.—The blue oxide tetrafluoride, $TcOF_4$, has been briefly reported[23] as being another by-product of the fluorination of technetium metal, the oxygen presumably coming from oxide films on the metal. It is very similar to its rhenium analogue, its magnetic moment (1.76 B.M. at $25°$, $\theta = 9°$) is as expected for a d^1 compound.

Rhenium Chlorides

Rhenium hexachloride.—There are reports in the literature of a volatile green chloride of rhenium which was thought to be the heptachloride or the hexachloride, but it was never characterized.[26, 27] No more was heard of the supposed green chloride after Geilmann *et al* announced the discovery of the brown pentachloride. Following the discovery of technetium hexachloride a literature search revealed that all workers who saw the green chloride made their rhenium by reduction methods and those who prepared the brown pentachloride used commercial rhenium powder.

Accordingly[28] rhenium metal was prepared by the reduction of ammonium perrhenate with hydrogen at 600°. After flushing the apparatus with purified nitrogen, chlorine was passed over the heated metal at 600°. On the small scale no rhenium pentachloride was observed, but a dark solid, melting very readily and giving a green vapour, was obtained. It could be readily distilled in the chlorine stream into a U tube cooled in ice/water mixture. Analysis showed the substance to be rhenium hexachloride.

The reaction of chlorine on a film of rhenium metal is thus similar to the action of chlorine on technetium metal (see below) and is in marked contrast to the action of chlorine on commercial rhenium powder (made from potassium perrhenate). It has also been shown however[28] that although the pentachloride is the major product with rhenium powder (previously heated in hydrogen to reduce surface oxides) and chlorine, some hexachloride also formed. It appears that some hexachloride has been present in most preparations of rhenium pentachloride.

The best way to prepare large amounts of rhenium hexachloride is to absorb ammonium perrhenate solution into porous brick material, dry and reduce to the metal with hydrogen at 600° and then to react it with a 1:1 mixture of chlorine and nitrogen at 650°.

Rhenium hexachloride forms long needles which are dichroic, appearing red brown by transmitted light and dark green by reflected light. The crystals melt at 25° to give a dark brownish liquid which volatilizes on gentle heating to a green vapour. In contrast to technetium hexachloride the compound is thermally stable in both nitrogen and chlorine and there is no indication of decomposition to the tetrachloride at 300°.

Hydrolysis of the hexachloride in alkali solution gave a precipitate of rhenium dioxide and soluble perrhenate ion in the ratio 1:2, agreeing with the usual hydrolysis scheme for Re^{VI} compounds[28]

$$3 \, Re^{VI} \rightarrow Re^{IV} + 2 \, Re^{VII}$$

When rhenium hexachloride is warmed in an atmosphere of oxygen the only product observed is perrhenyl chloride, ReO_3Cl.[28] In the fluoride system all three possible Re^{VII} oxide fluorides are known, but the only known oxide chloride of Re^{VII} is perrhenyl chloride. It was hoped that by gently oxidizing rhenium hexachloride an oxide chloride of Re^{VII}

containing more chlorine might be prepared, but none was obtained. The difference in reactivity of rhenium hexachloride and hexafluoride towards oxygen is noteworthy, rhenium hexafluoride can be heated in oxygen to 400° without reaction.[2]

Rhenium hexachloride obeys the Curie–Weiss Law closely over the range 300°K to 98°K.[29] The value of θ is 28° and the effective magnetic moment is 2.07 B.M. This value is to be compared with that of 0.25 B.M. obtained for the hexafluoride. The variation of susceptibility with temperature is given in Table 4-9.

Table 4-9. Magnetic properties of rhenium hexachloride

Temp (°K)	$\chi_M{}'$ (corr.) $\times 10^6$	μ (B.M.)
297	1695	2.01
266	1872	2.00
251	1982	1.99
225	2201	1.99
201	2403	1.97
177	2672	1.95
158	2942	1.93
134	3358	1.90
113	3876	1.87
98	4368	1.85

Rhenium pentachloride.—The pentachloride is the major product when chlorine reacts with rhenium powder (which has been previously heated in hydrogen to reduce oxide films) at 500–700°.[28, 30] The small amount of rhenium hexachloride also formed can be readily distilled out at a temperature lower than the melting point of the pentachloride.

Rhenium pentachloride can be purified by distillation in a stream of chlorine or by vacuum sublimation. Both of these procedures lead to the formation of small amounts of the trichloride which remains behind as an involatile residue.

Rhenium pentachloride is formed, together with the trichloride, by the thermal decomposition of silver hexachlororhenate (IV), Ag_2ReCl_6. There is no evidence for the formation of the tetrachloride which might be expected from this reaction.[30]

Rhenium pentachloride is a deep brown or black crystalline solid, m.p. 220°, which volatilizes easily to give a reddish brown vapour. It is instantly hydrolyzed by water showing the characteristic disproportionation reaction of Re^V to give Re^{IV} and Re^{VII}.

$$3\ Re^V \rightarrow 2\ Re^{IV} + Re^{VII}$$

It appears that an initial reaction product with water is hexachlororhenic acid, H_2ReCl_6[31] but in alkali solution the final products are the perrhenate ion and hydrated rhenium dioxide.

Rhenium pentachloride is a very reactive compound, although comparatively little use has been made of the compound as an intermediate or starting material in the preparative chemistry of rhenium.

Rhenium pentachloride reacts readily with oxygen to give oxide halides (see later) and when heated with potassium chloride it forms the hexachlororhenate (IV) ion.[32]

$$2 ReCl_5 + 4 KCl \rightarrow 2 K_2ReCl_6 + Cl_2$$

A rather ill-defined ammine complex said to be $[Re(NH_3)_6]Cl_5$ is formed by the reaction of liquid ammonia on the pentachloride.[33]

The magnetic properties of rhenium pentachloride have been investigated several times. Schuth and Klemm[34] found a moment of 2.3 B.M. for the solid compound on the basis of three measurements. Knox and Coffey[35] found that the pentachloride obeyed a Curie–Weiss Law to below 150°K giving $\mu_{eff} = 2.21$ B.M. and $\theta = 164$. More recently the susceptibility was remeasured[29] with a sample which had been carefully freed of any hexachloride and this sample gave a θ value of 266° agreeing precisely with that obtained by Schuth and Klemm although the actual susceptibilities were higher. It has been suggested[29] that the sample used by Knox and Coffey may have contained some rhenium hexachloride which would have lowered the value of θ observed. On the other hand, Knox and Coffey reported a divergence from the Curie–Weiss Law below 150° and this was confirmed by Brown and Colton who were able to show that the divergence occurred at about 110°K in a region where Knox and Coffey reported no results. The variation of susceptibility with temperature is given in Table 4-10.

Table 4-10. Magnetic properties of rhenium pentachloride

Knox and Coffey		Brown and Colton		
Temp (°K)	$\chi_M \times 10^6$	Temp (°K)	$\chi_M \times 10^6$	μ (B.M.)
301	1315	302	1457	1.88
253	1455	274	1524	1.83
196	1697	256	1591	1.81
150	1944	207	1746	1.70
79	2664	180	1840	1.63
—	—	154	1960	1.56
—	—	123	2120	1.45
—	—	99	2307	1.36
—	—	77	2606	1.27

Rhenium tetrachloride.—There are claims in the early literature to the preparation of rhenium tetrachloride[36] but none has been substantiated. It is noteworthy that reactions such as the thermal decomposition of Ag_2ReCl_6 that might be expected to give the tetrachloride actually gave mixtures of the pentachloride and trichloride. Rhenium tetraiodide and tetrabromide may be prepared by dehydrating the complex acids $H_2ReI_6 \cdot xH_2O$ and $H_2ReBr_6 \cdot xH_2O$ in a desiccator; two molecules of the halogen acid are also removed leaving the tetrahalides but the method fails for the tetrachloride as the complex acid does not decompose under these conditions.[31]

Rhenium tetrachloride has recently been prepared by the action of thionyl chloride on hydrated rhenium dioxide.[37] It was found necessary to prepare the dioxide by hydrolysis of rhenium pentachloride in water since hydrolysis of ammonium hexachlororhenate(IV) and other salts of this anion always gave dioxide containing large amounts of cationic impurities which in turn gave impure rhenium tetrachloride. The pure dioxide prepared in this way was separated, washed with water and acetone and vacuum dried.

After refluxing the dry oxide with thionyl chloride for several hours the supernatant liquid was a very dark green but experiment showed that in fact it contained very little rhenium and the bulk of the product was formed as a black insoluble solid. After centrifuging, the solid was vacuum dried.

Rhenium tetrachloride is a black solid which closely resembles rhenium tetraiodide. It is readily hydrolysed by moist air and must be handled in a dry box. On hydrolysis the compound forms some rhenium dioxide but like technetium tetrachloride it does not completely hydrolyse to the dioxide. The magnetic properties of rhenium tetrachloride have been investigated.[29, 37] Between 300°K and 220°K the Curie–Weiss Law is strictly obeyed but below 220°K the susceptibility rapidly increases. For the high temperature points $\theta = 158°$ and $\mu_{eff} = 1.55$ B.M.

More recently[68] the magnetic results have been interpreted on the assumption that rhenium tetrachloride consists of trimeric Re_3Cl_{12} species. A simple L.C.A.O.–M.O. treatment showed that if rhenium tetrachloride consisted of trimer units there should be one unpaired electron per trimer with a consequential magnetic moment of 1·0 B.M. per rhenium atom.

The variation with temperature of the magnetic susceptibility of rhenium tetrachloride is given in Table 4-11. Extrapolation to infinite temperature of a plot of molar susceptibility against reciprocal absolute temperature shows the presence of a substantial temperature independent contribution of 230×10^{-6}. A re-evaluation of the experimental data with the inclusion of this term reveals that the magnetic moment of rhenium

Table 4-11. Magnetic properties of rhenium tetrachloride

Temp ($°K$)	χ_M' (corr.) $\times 10^6$	$\mu(\text{B.M.}) = 2.84\ [(\chi_M - 230) \times 10^{-6}T)]^{\frac{1}{2}}$
304	654	1.02
275	695	1.02
255	730	1.01
240	766	1.02
215	807	1.00
189	888	1.00
158	1016	1.00
143	1132	1.02
123	1311	1.03
114	1418	1.04
96	1693	1.06
92	1840	1.09
87	2054	1.13

tetrachloride is 1 B.M. and virtually independent as required by the trimer model.

Other chemical evidence supporting the formulation of rhenium tetrachloride as a trimer was also presented[68].

Rhenium trichloride.—Rhenium trichloride is best prepared by the thermal decomposition of rhenium pentachloride in nitrogen,[30] a suitable apparatus is described by Hurd and Brimm.[39] Other methods of preparation are known but none is so convenient or so efficient. Sulphuryl chloride was found to react with rhenium powder with or without the addition of aluminium chloride to give very small amounts of rhenium trichloride.[40] The fact that yields were not increased by prolonged treatment suggests that it was in fact an oxide film which reacted with the sulphuryl chloride. Rhenium trichloride is also formed by the thermal decomposition of salts of hexachlororhenic(IV) acid.[32, 41]

Rhenium trichloride is a red crystalline compound. It is comparatively non-volatile but on strong heating it gives a green vapour and it can be sublimed slowly in a high vacuum at 500°. Rhenium trichloride is reduced by hydrogen to the metal at 250°–300° and with oxygen it gives perrhenyl chloride, ReO_3Cl and rhenium oxide tetrachloride, $ReOCl_4$.

Rhenium trichloride dissolves in acetone, methanol, acetic acid and similar solvents to give stable red solutions in which the trichloride is dimeric.[42, 43] In water rhenium trichloride gives a red solution and slowly hydrolyses, conductimetric experiments showed that the final hydrolysis product was the hydrated sesquioxide $Re_2O_3 \cdot xH_2O$.[30]

Rhenium trichloride solutions in hydrochloric acid are very stable. Wrigge and Biltz suggested that the tetrachlororhenate(III) ion, $ReCl_4^-$ is

F

formed and they claimed to have isolated salts containing this ion,[44] but more recent work has shown that the situation is more complicated than this and involves the formation of polymeric products.[44, 45] (See Chapter five.)

Rhenium trichloride dissolves in liquid ammonia and investigation of the vapour pressure isotherms suggested the presence of $ReCl_3 \cdot 14NH_3$; $ReCl_3 \cdot 7NH_3$ and $ReCl_3 \cdot 6NH_3$.[33] No recent work has been done on this system which may be worthy of further study.

Schuth and Klemm[34] found that rhenium trichloride had a very small temperature-independent paramagnetism, but a later determination by Knox and Coffey[35] gave higher values of the susceptibility which varied slightly with temperature. It had been noticed[31] that rhenium trichloride prepared from rhenium pentachloride and used without further treatment was chemically reactive, but if it were vacuum sublimed at 500°c it became comparatively unreactive. It has recently been shown[46] that the low temperature form of rhenium trichloride has a molar susceptibility corresponding to that measured by Schuth and Klemm ($\approx 20 \times 10^{-6}$ c.g.s.) and the vacuum sublimed material (high temperature form) has a susceptibility corresponding to that measured by Knox and Coffey ($\approx 495 \times 10^{-6}$ c.g.s.). However, no detectable structure difference between the two forms could be observed by x-ray diffraction techniques.

The heat of oxidation of rhenium trichloride according to the equation

$$ReCl_3(s) + 4\,OH^- + 2\,OCl^- \rightarrow ReO_4^- + 2\,H_2O + 5\,Cl^-$$

was determined by placing a small bulb containing the trichloride in a calorimeter with a known amount of standardized hypochlorite solution. On breaking the bulb the rhenium was oxidized. The heat of oxidation of rhenium trichloride was found to be 190.7 ± 0.2 kcal/mole.[62]

Rhenium Oxide Chlorides

There are only two oxide chlorides of rhenium known, perrhenyl chloride ReO_3Cl, and rhenium oxide tetrachloride. It is worth comparing the lack of Re^{VII} oxide chlorides with the existence of all three possible Re^{VII} oxide fluorides. Reactions which might reasonably be expected to give either ReO_2Cl_3 or $ReOCl_5$, for instance, the action of oxygen on rhenium pentachloride or hexachloride, give only perrhenyl chloride and usually also rhenium oxide tetrachloride.

Rhenium trioxide chloride (*perrhenyl chloride*).—Perrhenyl chloride was first prepared by Brukl and Ziegler [47] by chlorinating rhenium metal to give a volatile chloride which was then allowed to react with rhenium heptaoxide. By fractionating the product in nitrogen they were able to separate perrhenyl chloride as a colourless, highly refractive liquid from rhenium oxide tetrachloride which was the other product of the reaction. The same two oxide chlorides are also formed by the action of oxygen on rhenium trichloride.[30, 48] It has been claimed[49] that oxygen and rhenium pentachloride gave rhenium dioxide trichloride, ReO_2Cl_3, but it has recently been shown[31] that the products of the reaction are in fact perrhenyl chloride and rhenium oxide tetrachloride. The alleged ReO_2Cl_3 was probably a mixture of the two compounds. Perrhenyl chloride is also formed by the action of oxygen on both rhenium hexachloride and rhenium oxide tetrachloride.[47] Possibly the best method of preparation of perrhenyl chloride is to chlorinate rhenium trioxide at 160°–190°. After removal of dissolved chlorine by vacuum distillation this method is said to give a very pure product.[50]

Perrhenyl chloride is a colourless compound, m.p. 4.5°, the boiling point being given as 131°[47] and 128°.[50] The compound is stable in dry air but it is instantly hydrolysed by water to give only perrhenic and hydrochloric acids.[47] It is very reactive and is decomposed by mercury, silver and stopcock grease to give rhenium trioxide.[50] The infra-red spectrum of perrhenyl chloride shows a band at 10.4 μ attributed to the Re=O stretch. From a study of the microwave spectrum of perrhenyl chloride Amble and coworkers[51] were able to show that the molecule was a symmetrical top and they derived the following parameters:

$$Re-O = 1.761 \pm 0.003 \text{ Å}$$
$$Re-Cl = 2.230 \pm 0.004 \text{ Å}$$
$$Cl-Re-Cl = 108° 20' \pm 1°$$

Rhenium oxide tetrachloride.—Little fresh information on rhenium oxide tetrachloride has been published since soon after its discovery by Brukl and Ziegler[47] who obtained it as the second product of the reaction between a rhenium chloride and rhenium heptaoxide. Other methods of preparation are mentioned in the section on perrhenyl chloride.

The melting point of the compound seems to be a matter of some doubt. Brukl and Ziegler[47] reported that it melts at 29–30.5°, whilst Kolling, who made it by the action of oxygen on rhenium trichloride, observed a melting point of 34°.[48] Determination of the boiling point by the same workers gave values of 223° and 225° respectively.

Rhenium oxide tetrachloride is a brown crystalline solid which melts to give a brown liquid. The vapour is greenish brown, intermediate between the colours of the vapours of rhenium pentachloride (brown) and rhenium hexachloride (green). The compound fumes in air and is instantly hydrolysed by water to give perrhenic acid (2 parts) and rhenium dioxide (1 part) in accordance with the usual disproportion reaction for Re^{VI} compounds.

$$3 \text{ ReOCl}_4 + 7 \text{ H}_2\text{O} \rightarrow 2 \text{ HReO}_4 + \text{ReO}_2 + 12 \text{ HCl}$$

Brukl and Ziegler[47] reported that rhenium oxide tetrachloride dissolved in cold concentrated hydrochloric acid to give a brown solution which may contain the complex acid $H_2\text{ReOCl}_6$ since they claimed to have isolated the salt $K_2\text{ReOCl}_6$ from the solution.

Some interesting, but unconfirmed, observations on the behaviour of rhenium oxide tetrachloride in carbon tetrachloride solution have been reported by Brukl and Plettinger.[53] They found that on careful addition of water to these solutions a blue precipitate was formed which had a Re:Cl ratio of 1:2 with varying amounts of oxygen and hydroxyl groups, but the product was never properly characterized. These workers also claimed that cold dry ammonia gas reacted with rhenium oxide tetra-chloride to give $\text{ReO}(\text{NH}_2)_2\text{Cl}_2$.

The magnetic moment of rhenium oxide tetrachloride was measured some years ago and a value of $\mu_\text{eff} = 1.5$ B.M. was obtained.[34]

Technetium Chlorides

Technetium hexachloride.—The first reported study of the chlorides and oxide chlorides of technetium was made by Nelson, Boyd and Smith.[54] They found, rather surprisingly, that chlorine gas had no action on technetium metal even on heating for a considerable time. However their experiments were conducted in a closed static system and it has since been found that technetium reacts readily with chlorine at moderate tempera-tures if a flow of gas is maintained over the heated metal.[55] This difference in behaviour in static and dynamic systems is so dramatic for technetium that an investigation was made of the chlorination of rhenium in a static system. In this case it was readily observed[31] that a cloud of dark brown vapour of rhenium pentachloride was readily formed above the metal and this obviously prevented more chlorine reaching the metal. As soon as a gas flow was introduced the vapour of the pentachloride was swept away allowing further attack of the metal. It seems clear that similar considerations apply in the case of technetium. The chlorination of techne-tium metal in a stream of chlorine yields two products, the first is a volatile green compound which was shown to be technetium hexachloride. Techne-tium hexachloride is an extremely unstable compound, it decomposes to the tetrachloride even on very gentle warming and samples sealed in an atmosphere of chlorine gas decomposed completely to the tetrachloride in 24 hours. Technetium hexachloride melts at about 25° and it is quite volatile. It was possible to separate it from the tetrachloride also formed during the chlorination of the metal by distilling at room temperature in a rapid stream of nitrogen and collecting it in a tube cooled in ice. Several distillations were necessary to remove dissolved chlorine which appears to be quite soluble in the liquid hexachloride. Technetium hexachloride was characterized by analysis which showed a ratio of technetium to chlorine of $1:6$ and also by demonstrating that the compound hydrolysed in the manner expected of a compound of Tc^{VI}.

$$3\ Tc^{VI} \rightarrow 2\ Tc^{VII} + Tc^{IV}$$

The technetium dioxide was separated and it was shown that the proportions of pertechnetate and dioxide formed were in the proportions required by the equation.[55]

Technetium tetrachloride.—The major product of the chlorination of technetium metal is technetium tetrachloride, this red compound is quite stable and it is easily purified by sublimation at about 300° in a gentle stream of chlorine or nitrogen.[55] Technetium tetrachloride was first prepared however by the interaction of technetium heptaoxide with carbon tetrachloride in a sealed tube at about 400°.[56]

Technetium tetrachloride dissolves in hydrochloric acid to give yellow solutions containing the hexachlorotechnate (IV) anion. Its behaviour in water and alkali solution is similar to rhenium tetrachloride; it is not instantly hydrolysed, indeed it is difficult to completely hydrolyse both compounds.

The magnetic behaviour of technetium tetrachloride has been studied over a temperature range but only five measurements are recorded.[35] The plot of the reciprocal of the corrected molar susceptibility against the absolute temperature was not linear, the three points at the higher temperatures were taken to give a crude Curie–Weiss plot from which the values of $\mu = 3.14$ B.M. and $\theta = -57°$ were obtained. In view of the rather unusual negative value of θ and the great difference between the magnetic behaviour of technetium tetrachloride and rhenium tetrachloride it would be desirable for a more detailed study of the magnetic behaviour of the technetium compound to be made.

Technetium Oxide Chlorides

Technetium trioxide chloride (pertechnyl chloride).—Pertechnyl chloride, TcO_3Cl, was said to have been formed by treating potassium pertechnetate dissolved in 18 M sulphuric acid with 12 M hydrochloric acid.[57] It was found that the compound could be extracted into chloroform, carbon tetrachloride and hexane and although its vibrational spectrum was recorded there is no record of it having been isolated and characterized.

More recently however, pertechnyl chloride has been isolated by gently heating technetium tetrachloride in a stream of oxygen.[31] Pertechnyl chloride, like its rhenium analogue is a colourless liquid. It is less stable however than the rhenium compound, gentle heating causes some decomposition to a red solid although the bulk of the liquid distilled unchanged. Heating the red solid in a stream of chlorine gave pertechnyl chloride again and it is thought that the solid is technetium trioxide, the decomposition of pertechnyl chloride thus resembles the decomposition of perrhenyl bromide (see later).

Technetium oxide tetrachloride.—Two products which were thought to have been oxide chlorides of technetium were observed during the reaction between chlorine and technetium dioxide.[54] The first product sublimed at 80–90° and the second brown product could be sublimed at 500°. Neither of these compounds were characterized at this time although it was noted that both were paramagnetic. It has since been suggested[58] that the brown compound was technetium oxide trichloride $TcOCl_3$. This has recently been confirmed by the author[31] and it appears very likely that the blue compound is technetium oxide tetrachloride $TcOCl_4$. Again the decomposition of the technetium oxide chloride may be compared with the behaviour of the corresponding rhenium oxide bromide[59] which decomposes in a similar way.

Technetium oxide trichloride.—Technetium oxide trichloride is rather involatile, subliming at about 500° in a vacuum. This low volatility is a common feature of this type of pentavalent compound of these metals and it appears likely that they have structures similar to niobium oxide trichloride.

Technetium oxide trichloride hydrolyses in accordance with the expected behaviour of a compound of pentavalent technetium[31]

$$3\,Tc^V \rightarrow 2\,Tc^{IV} + Tc^{VII}$$

Rhenium Bromides

Rhenium pentabromide.—Rhenium pentabromide is the major product if bromine vapour is carried in a stream of nitrogen over rhenium at 650°,[59] although a previous report claimed that the tribromide was the product formed at 450°.[60] There is no evidence of the formation of a hexabromide if a freshly reduced film of rhenium metal is used. Rhenium pentabromide is a dark blue solid which melts a little above room temperature to give a bluish green liquid, the vapour is deep blue. On heating in vacuum or in nitrogen, rhenium pentabromide decomposes in the same way as the pentachloride, although rather more readily, to give the tribromide.[59]

Rhenium tetrabromide.—Rhenium tetrabromide may be prepared by reduction of perrhenic acid with hydrobromic acid[61] or by dissolution of rhenium dioxide in hydrobromic acid. The best method is to treat rhenium tetraiodide with successive portions of hydrobromic acid with evaporation to a small volume between each addition.[31] In all these methods the product is finally dried in a desiccator containing potassium hydroxide and phosphorus pentoxide.

Rhenium tribromide.—Rhenium tribromide may be prepared by the thermal decomposition of the pentabromide[59] or silver hexabromorhenate (IV).[62] It is a reddish brown solid and like rhenium trichloride it is fairly involatile. Rhenium tribromide is soluble in hydrobromic acid and polar organic solvents and in these media its spectrum resembles that of the trichloride which suggests that in the acid media complexes of the type $ReBr_4^-$ similar to $ReCl_4^-$ may be formed, although these were not isolated.[59] Using hypochlorite as already described for rhenium trichloride the heat of oxidation of the tribromide was found to be 204.7 $\pm$ 0.5 kcal/mole[1].[62]

Rhenium Oxide Bromides

Rhenium trioxide bromide (perrhenyl bromide).—Perrhenyl bromide, ReO_3Br, may be prepared by the action of bromine vapour on potassium perrhenate,[61] by the action of bromine on rhenium trioxide,[51] or by the action of bromine on rhenium heptaoxide.[63] It is a colourless compound which is readily decomposed thermally to the trioxide,[61] a very unusual type of decomposition which has also been observed for pertechnyl chloride.[31]

The infra-red spectrum of perrhenyl bromide has been observed; it is very similar to that of perrhenyl chloride and the following assignments were made[64]

ν_6 168 cm^{-1}	ν_2 350 cm^{-1}
ν_3 195 cm^{-1}	ν_4 963 cm^{-1}
ν_5 332 cm^{-1}	ν_1 997 cm^{-1}

Rhenium oxide tetrabromide.—The blue compound formulated as rhenium dioxide dibromide, ReO_2Br_2, has been shown in fact to be rhenium oxide tetrabromide,[59] $ReOBr_4$. It is made by any one of several reactions, for example rhenium metal heated in a bromine/oxygen stream, rhenium heptaoxide and bromine vapour, rhenium tetrabromide and oxygen and best of all, anhydrous rhenium dioxide and bromine vapour. Rhenium oxide tetrabromide is a blue solid with a low melting point and on heating is thermally decomposed to rhenium oxide tribromide, $ReOBr_3$.

Technetium Oxide Bromides

Only one oxide bromide of technetium has been prepared so far. Bromine vapour reacts with technetium dioxide at about 350° to give a brown sublimate of technetium oxide tribromide $TcOBr_3$.[31] The corresponding reaction with rhenium dioxide gives rhenium oxide tetrabromide.[59] Technetium oxide tribromide is rather involatile but quite stable thermally. It is instantly hydrolysed by water or alkali, pertechnatate and technetium dioxide are produced in the proportions expected.

$$3 Tc^V \rightarrow 2 Tc^{IV} + Tc^{VII}$$

Rhenium Iodides

Rhenium tetraiodide.—The Noddacks[65] claimed to have prepared rhenium tetraiodide by passing iodine vapour over heated rhenium metal, but other workers have failed to repeat the preparation by this method.[40, 65] It was found that there was no interaction between rhenium and iodine in a sealed tube at 170°–180° or between rhenium powder and iodine in refluxing carbon tetrachloride.[40] It is now known that rhenium tetraiodide is thermally unstable and none of these methods can be expected to give the desired compound.

Rhenium tetraiodide was finally prepared by the reduction of perrhenic acid with hydriodic acid at room temperature.[66] Iodine is released in the reaction and an intermediate, which is probably a hydrate of hexaiodorhenic acid, is the first product obtained as the solution is evaporated to dryness. The intermediate compound loses water and hydriodic acid on standing in a desiccator with alkali and phosphorus (v) oxide to give rhenium tetraiodide.

Rhenium tetraiodide is a rather unstable compound, it loses iodine slowly in a vacuum at room temperature and rapidly on heating. It is very hygroscopic and dissolves in water to give a brown solution which rapidly hydrolyses giving rhenium dioxide, but rather more stable brown solutions are obtained in acetone and ether.

Although rhenium tetraiodide appears to be crystalline, it is almost amorphous and no x-ray diffraction pattern has been obtained from the compound. The magnetic moment has been reported as 0.9 B.M.[32] but no details of the susceptibility or θ value were given.

Rhenium tri-iodide.—Rhenium tri-iodide was prepared[65] by the thermal decomposition of the tetraiodide in a sealed tube at 350°. It may also be prepared by the thermal decomposition of ammonium hexaiodorhenate (IV) at 325° *in vacuo* and heating the residue with iodine in a sealed tube at 200°.[66] A more recent and direct method is the reduction of perrhenic acid with hydriodic acid and alcohol at elevated temperatures.[67] The crystals are washed with alcohol and carbon tetrachloride.

Rhenium triiodide is only slightly soluble in water and dilute acids and almost insoluble in alcohol, acetone and ether. It slowly loses iodine in vacuum, especially if heated.[65]

Rhenium diiodide.—Rhenium diiodide was prepared by heating the tetraiodide for 6 hours in a sealed tube at 350° in an atmosphere of carbon dioxide.[38] The iodine was extracted with carbon tetrachloride. The magnetic moment was given as 0.5 B.M. and it is likely that rhenium–rhenium interaction occurs in this compound.

Rhenium moniodide.—Rhenium moniodide was prepared by heating rhenium tetraiodide to constant weight in a stream of nitrogen in the presence of a little iodine at 200°.[65] X-ray diffraction revealed a simple cubic lattice (a = 9.33 Å). Rhenium moniodide combines with iodine in a sealed tube at 200° to give the triiodide. In vacuum it is thermally decomposed to the metal.[65] The magnetic moment is given as 0.6 B.M.[38]

References

1. J. G. MALM, H. SELIG and S. FRIED, *J. Am. Chem. Soc.* **82**, 1510 (1960).
2. J. G. MALM and H. SELIG, *J. Inorg. Nucl. Chem.* **20**, 189 (1961).
3. O. RUFF, W. KWASNIK and E. ASCHER, *Z. Anorg. Allgem. Chem.* **209**, 113 (1932).
4. O. RUFF, *Z. Angew. Chem.* **46**, 239 (1933).
5. O. RUFF and W. KWASNIK, *Z. Anorg. Allgem. Chem.* **220**, 96 (1934).
6. N. S. NIKOLAEV and E. G. IPPOLITOV, *Dokl. Akad. Nauk SSSR* **134**, 358 (1960).
7. G. H. CADY and G. B. HARGREAVES, *J. Chem. Soc.* 1563 (1961).
8. J. GAUNT, *Trans. Faraday Soc.* **50**, 209 (1954).
9. H. H. CLAASSEN, J. G. MALM and H. SELIG, *J. Chem. Phys.* **36**, 2890 (1962).
10. H. SELIG, F. A. CAFASSO, D. N. GRUEN and J. G. MALM, *J. Chem, Phys.* **36**, 3440 (1962).
11. G. B. HARGREAVES and R. D. PEACOCK, *J. Chem. Soc.* 1099 (1960).
12. G. H. CADY and G. B. HARGREAVES, *J. Chem. Soc.* 1568 (1961).
13. H. J. EMELEUS and V. GUTMAN, *J. Chem. Soc.* 2115 (1950).
14. E. E. AYNSLEY, R. D. PEACOCK and P. L. ROBINSON, *J. Chem. Soc.* 1622 (1950).
15. A. ENGELBRECHT and A. V. GROSSE, *J. Am. Chem. Soc.* **76**, 2042 (1954).
16. E. E. AYNSLEY and M. L. HAIR, *J. Chem. Soc.* 3747 (1958).
17. J. F. LOTSPEICH, A. JAVAN and A. ENGELBRECHT, *J. Chem. Phys.* **31**, 633 (1959).
18. M. KOTANI, *J. Phys. Soc. (Japan)* **4**, 293 (1949).
19. H. SELIG, C. H. CHERNICK and J. G. MALM, *J. Inorg. Nucl. Chem.* **19**, 377 (1961).
20. H. SELIG and J. G. MALM, *J. Inorg. Nucl. Chem.* **24**, 641 (1962).
21. H. H. CLAASSEN, H. SELIG and J. G. MALM, *J. Chem. Phys.* **36**, 2288 (1962).

22. H. Selig and J. G. Malm, Personal communication quoted by R. Colton and R. D. Peacock, *Quart. Rev. London* **16**, 310 (1962).
23. A. J. Edwards, D. Hugill and R. D. Peacock, *Nature* **200**, 672 (1963).
24. J. R. Sites, C. R. Baldock and L. O. Gilpatrick, *Unclassified Document* ORNL 1327 (1952).
25. H. Selig and J. G. Malm, *J. Inorg. Nucl. Chem.* **25**, 349 (1963).
26. F. Schacheral, *Chem. Listy* **23**, 632 (1929).
27. W. Noddack, *Z. Elektrochem.* **34**, 627 (1928).
28. R. Colton, *Nature* **194**, 374 (1962).
29. D. Brown and R. Colton, *J. Chem. Soc.* 714 (1964).
30. W. Geilmann, F. W. Wrigge and W. Biltz, *Z. Anorg. Allgem. Chem.* **214**, 248 (1933).
31. R. Colton, Unpublished observations.
32. H. V. A. Briscoe, P. L. Robinson and C. M. Stoddart, *J. Chem. Soc.* 2263 (1931).
33. W. Klemm and G. Frischmuth, *Z. Anorg. Allgem. Chem.* **230**, 209 (1937).
34. W. Schuth and W. Klemm, *Z. Anorg. Allgem. Chem.* **220**, 193 (1934).
35. K. Knox and C. E. Coffey, *J. Am. Chem. Soc.* **81**, 5 (1959).
36. D. M. Yost and G. Schull, *J. Am. Chem. Soc.* **54**, 4657 (1932).
37. D. Brown and R. Colton, *Nature* **198**, 1300 (1963).
38. J. E. Fergusson, B. H. Robinson and W. R. Roper, *J. Chem. Soc.* 2113 (1962).
39. L. C. Hurd and E. Brimm, *Inorganic Syntheses* Vol. I, 182 (1939).
40. C. L. Rulfs and P. J. Elving, *J. Am. Chem. Soc.* **72**, 3304 (1950).
41. T. Mao and V. G. Tronev, *Zh. Neorgan. Khim.* **4**, 1768 (1959).
42. F. W. Wrigge and W. Biltz, *Z. Anorg. Allgem. Chem.* **228**, 372 (1936).
43. R. S. Nyholm, Private Communication.
44. W. T. Robinson, J. E. Fergusson and B. R. Penfold, *Proc. Chem. Soc.* 116 (1963).
45. J. A. Bertrand, F. A. Cotton and W. A. Dollase, *J. Am. Chem. Soc.* **85**, 1349 (1963).
46. D. Brown and R. Colton, to be published.
47. A. Bruckl and K. Ziegler, *Chem. Ber.* **65B**, 916 (1932).
48. O. W. Kolling, *Trans. Kansas Acad. Sci.* **56**, 378 (1953).
49. H. V. A. Briscoe, P. L. Robinson and A. J. Rudge, *J. Chem. Soc.* 1104 (1932).
50. C. J. Wolf, A. F. Clifford and W. H. Johnston, *J. Am. Chem. Soc.* **79**, 4257 (1957).
51. E. Amble, S. L. Miller, A. L. Schawlaw and C. H. Townes, *J. Chem. Phys.* **20**, 192 (1952).
52. D. Brown and R. Colton, *J. Chem. Soc.* (in press).
53. A. Bruckl and E. Plettinger, *Chem. Ber.* **65B**, 971 (1933).
54. C. M. Nelson, G. E. Boyd and W. T. Smith, *J. Am. Chem. Soc.* **76**, 348 (1954).
55. R. Colton, *Nature* **193**, 872 (1962).
56. K. Knox, S. Y. Tyree, R. M. Srivastava, V. Norman, J. Y. Bassett and J. H. Holloway, *J. Am. Chem. Soc.* **79**, 3358 (1957).
57. R. H. Busey and Q. V. Larson, *Unclassified Document* O.R.N.L. 2584 (1959).
58. G. E. Boyd, *J. Chem. Educ.* **36**, 7 (1959).
59. R. Colton, *J. Chem. Soc.* **2072** (1962).

60. H. HAGAN and A. SIEVERTS, *Z. Anorg. Allgem. Chem.* **215**, 111 (1933).
61. R. COLTON and G. WILKINSON, *Chem. Ind. London* **1314** (1959).
62. J. P. KING and J. W. COBBLE, *J. Am. Chem. Soc.* **82**, 2111 (1960).
63. A. BRUCKL and K. ZIEGLER, *Monatsh. Chem.* **63**, 329 (1933).
64. F. A. MILLER and G. L. CARLSON, *Spectrochim. Acta* **116**, 1148 (1960).
65. I. and W. NODDACK, *Das Rhenium* Leipzig (1933).
66. R. D. PEACOCK, A. J. E. WELCH and L. F. WILSON, *J. Chem. Soc.* 2901 (1958).
67. L. MALATESTA, *Inorganic Syntheses* Vol. 7, 185 (1963).
68. R. COTTON and R. L. Martin, *Nature*, **205**, 239 (1965).

5

Complex Halides

There is a number of reported complex halides of rhenium, some very well established, others not so certain. The most studied compounds are those of the type K_2ReX_6 where X is any one of the halogens. Many of the reported chlorocomplexes can be regarded as hydrolysis products of the hexachlororhenate(IV) ion. The tetrachlororhenate(III) ion with its unique structure has no known analogue with the other halogens although there is some evidence that the corresponding bromide exists in solution. The only technetium compounds that have been well studied are those of the K_2TcX_6 type. Complex halides and complex oxide halides will be treated together.

Rhenium Complex Fluorides

Hexafluororhenates(IV).—Ruff and Kwasnik[1] claimed to have prepared the hexafluororhenate(IV) ion, $ReF_6{}^{2-}$, by the action of 40% hydrogen fluoride on potassium perrhenate in the presence of potassium iodide. This is a general method for the preparation of the other hexahalorhenates but later workers have failed to prepare the complex fluoride by this method.[2, 3]

Weise[2] prepared the compound by treating the corresponding hexabromorhenate with hydrogen fluoride at 450°. It was found that the compound has a trigonal structure and not the cubic K_2PtCl_6 structure as reported by Ruff and Kwasnik.

Potassium hexafluororhenate(IV) may also be prepared by the action of ammonium hexaiodorhenate(IV) with potassium hydrogen fluoride at 250°.[3] The crude salt, after separation from the more soluble potassium fluoride and potassium iodide, was recrystallized from hot water.[3]

Other salts of the hexafluororhenate (IV) ion have been prepared by neutralizing the free acid, prepared from the potassium salt by ion exchange.[9] The fluororhenates (IV) are generally resistant to hydrolysis although the silver and copper salts decompose if their solutions are evaporated to dryness. Although a solution of the free acid is stable in the cold for several weeks, a solid cannot be isolated due to decomposition

$$H_2ReF_6 + H_2O \rightarrow ReO_2 + 4\,HF$$

The salts which have been isolated together with their solubilities are shown in Table 5-1. The salts are not easily attacked by alkalis and only slowly oxidized by hydrogen peroxide. Electrolytic reduction gives the metal.

Table 5-1. The hexafluororhenates(IV)

Salt	Colour	Solubility
Na_2ReF_6	white	v. sol. hot and cold
$(NH_4)_2ReF_6$	white	v. sol. hot and cold
K_2ReF_6	white	v. sol. hot, sol. cold
Rb_2ReF_6	white	sol. hot, s. sol. cold
Cs_2ReF_6	white	sol. hot, s. sol. cold
$BaReF_6$	white	sol. only when freshly pptd.
$[Ni(NH_3)_4]ReF_6$	purple	s. sol.
$[Cr(NH_3)_6]_2(ReF_6)_3$	red-brown	s. sol.

Crystallographically the fluororhenates (IV) resemble the complex fluorides of manganese and the platinum metals. The alkali salts (except Na) are trigonal. The barium salt is isomorphous with the corresponding fluoroosmate (IV) and fluoroiridate (IV). The crystallographic details together with those of the corresponding fluoroplatinates (IV) for comparison are shown in Table 5-2.

Table 5-2. Crystallographic data for the fluororhenates(IV)[4]

Compound	Symmetry	Unit cells (Å)	
		Fluororhenates	Fluoroplatinates
Na_2ReF_6	Tetragonal		(trigonal)
	(possibly pseudo-cubic)	$a_0 = 10.02$ $c_0 = 10.14$	$a_0 = 9.41$ $c_0 = 5.16$
K_2ReF_6	Trigonal	$a_0 = 5.86$ $c_0 = 4.60$	$a_0 = 5.76$ $c_0 = 4.64$
Rb_2ReF_6	Trigonal	$a_0 = 6.01$ $c_0 = 4.77$	$a_0 = 5.96$ $c_0 = 4.83$
$(NH_4)_2ReF_6$	Trigonal	$a_0 = 6.06$ $c_0 = 4.77$	— —
Cs_2ReF_6	Trigonal	$a_0 = 6.32$ $c_0 = 4.99$	$a_0 = 6.22$ $c_0 = 5.01$
$BaReF_6$	Rhombohedral	$a_0 = 4.92$ $\alpha = 97°25'$	$a_0 = 4.90$ $\alpha = 97°8'$
			(BaIrF_6)

The magnetic properties of potassium and caesium hexafluoro-rhenates (IV) have been studied over a wide temperature range.[5] The compounds obey the Curie–Weiss law with $\theta = 40°$ and $\mu_{calc\ 300°} = 3.30$ B.M. for the potassium salt and $\theta = 24$ and $\mu_{300°} = 3.32$ B.M. for the caesium salt. In aqueous solution potassium hexafluororhenate has a magnetic moment of 3.43 B.M. at room temperature.

Hexafluororhenates (V).—The hexafluororhenate (V) ion has been prepared by the reduction of rhenium hexafluoride with potassium iodide in liquid sulphur dioxide.[6] Excess hexafluoride was used so that potassium hexafluororhenate (V) was the only involatile product of the reaction and it could be purified by pumping. The hexafluororhenates (V) are white crystalline powders which attack glass at 300°. They are very sensitive to moisture and darken on exposure to the air. Water and alkalis cause vigorous hydrolysis giving a precipitate of hydrated rhenium dioxide, the supernatant solution contains fluoride, perrhenate and hexafluoro-rhenate (IV).[6]

Crystallographically the hexafluororhenates (V) resemble the corresponding salts of antimony, niobium and tantalum rather than those of osmium and the other platinum metals. The unit cell dimensions indicate that Re^{5+} is about the same size as Sb^{5+}; for $NaReF_6$ $a_0 = 8.18$ Å but for $KReF_6$ there is a slight tetragonal distortion $a_0 = 10.26$ and $c_0 = 10.01$ Å, similar to that found for other potassium salts of the general type KMF_6[6] and this distortion is reflected in the rather different magnetic properties of the potassium compound.

The magnetic properties of the 'alkali hexafluororhenates (V) have been studied over a wide temperature range.[7] The compounds do not behave as predicted by the Kotani theory for a d^2 system and considerable anti-ferromagnetic interactions may occur in the solid. Although no Néel points were observed for these compounds in the temperature range studied, the corresponding tungsten compounds did show Néel points confirming that antiferromagnetic interactions are possible in this type of compound. The magnetic moments obtained were

	θ	μ_{300} (B.M.)
$NaReF_6$	100	1.57
$KReF_6$	58	2.05
$RbReF_6$	50	1.56
$CsReF_6$	35	1.53

Fluoro complexes of Re^{VI}.—Eight-coordinate fluoro complexes have recently been obtained by the interaction of rhenium hexafluoride and potassium fluoride.[8] Addition of potassium fluoride to rhenium hexa-fluoride cooled to 0° in a Teflon tube caused considerable evolution of heat. After all the fluoride had dissolved the tube was sealed and heated to 20°, and after several hours the excess hexafluoride was pumped off leaving a residue of octafluororhenate (VI)

$$ReF_6 + 2 KF \rightarrow K_2ReF_8$$

The orange crystals were almost insoluble in water and were only slowly hydrolysed to a blue compound. They dissolved in hydrofluoric acid with decomposition.

$$K_2ReF_8 + nHF \rightarrow ReF_6 + 2 KF \cdot nHF$$

The same workers also claimed in a later communication[9] that all the alkali fluorides (except Li) react further with rhenium hexafluoride

$$ReF_6 + 2 MF \rightarrow M_2ReF_8$$
$$M_2ReF_8 + ReF_6 \rightarrow 2 MReF_7$$

The thermal stability of the heptafluororhenates decreased in the series $Cs > Rb > K > Na$, $KReF_7$ dissociates at 50°.

The magnetic moments of the octafluororhenates were given as 1.6–1.7 B.M. and those of the heptafluorides as 0.6–0.7 B.M.

The octafluororhenates gradually turn blue in air or in water, the blue compound has been shown to be an oxide fluoride.[10]

$$M_2ReF_8 + H_2O \rightarrow MReOF_5 + MF \cdot 2HF$$

The oxide fluorides were best prepared by grinding the octafluororhenates in a platinum dish. The caesium salt rapidly became blue and viscous, but as the potassium and rubidium salts were rather more stable it was neces-sary to add 99% hydrofluoric acid to them. After turning blue, the product was washed with methanol and extracted with methyl ethyl ketone. The evaporated solution yielded the crystalline complex oxide fluorides. They were all soluble in water and organic solvents although the aqueous solutions rapidly turned brown due to hydrolysis. The valency of rhenium in $CsReOF_5$ was shown to be six and the magnetic moment was given as 1.48 B.M.

Fluoro complexes of Re^{VII}.—Complex oxide fluorides of Re^{VII} have been prepared by the action of bromine trifluoride on potassium perrhenate.[11] On dissolving the perrhenate oxygen and bromine were evolved. After reaction had ceased the excess bromine trifluoride was removed under vacuum leaving a cream residue which analysis showed to be potassium dioxotetrafluororhenate (VII) $KReO_2F_4$. The compound was very hygroscopic, water quickly hydrolysed it and alkali caused immediate hydrolysis. By using other perrhenates the corresponding rubidium, caesium, silver and barium salts were prepared.[11]

Technetium Complex Fluorides

Hexafluorotechnates (IV).—Pink potassium hexafluorotechnate (IV), K_2TcF_6, has been obtained by the reaction of both potassium hexachlorotechnate (IV)[12] or hexabromotechnate (IV)[13] with potassium hydrogen fluoride melts. The fluorotechnate anion, like its rhenium analogue, is quite resistant to hydrolysis and may be purified by recrystallization from water. The complex must be heated in concentrated alkali solution to bring about hydrolysis.[13] The free acid, as well as other fluorotechnates, have been prepared from the potassium salt by ion exchange procedures.[12] The sodium and ammonium salts are very soluble and the barium salt, again like its rhenium analogue, becomes less soluble on ageing.

Potassium hexafluorotechnate(IV) has a trigonal lattice isostructural with potassium hexafluororhenate(IV) (K_2GeF_6 structure), with $a = 5.807 \pm0.002$ and $c = 4.645 \pm 0.002$ Å.[13]

The infra-red spectrum of potassium hexafluorotechnate (IV) shows a band at 574 cm^{-1} which has been assigned to the metal–fluorine stretch.[13]

Hexafluorotechnates (V).—The reduction of technetium hexafluoride in iodine pentafluoride has led to the isolation of other complex fluorides of technetium.[14] The action of potassium iodide in iodine pentafluoride leads to a quadrivalent species which is probably potassium pentafluorotechnate (IV), $KTcF_5$, the corresponding reduction with rhenium hexafluoride gave potassium hexafluororhenate (V), $KReF_6$. However, sodium and potassium hexafluorotechnates (V) were prepared by the action of solutions of alkali chlorides on technetium hexafluoride in iodine pentafluoride.[14] These yellow compounds were isostructural with the corresponding ruthenium salts but not with the corresponding fluororhenates (V) as shown in Table 5-3.

Table 5-3. Lattice constants of some complex fluorides

$NaReF_6$	Cubic	$a = 8.18$ Å	—
$NaTcF_6$	Rhombohedral	$a = 5.77$ Å	$\alpha = 55.8°$
$NaRuF_6$	Rhombohedral	$a = 5.80$ Å	$\alpha = 54.5°$
$KReF_6$	Tetragonal	$a = 10.01$ Å	$c = 5.13$ Å
$KTcF_6$	Rhombohedral	$a = 4.97$ Å	$\alpha = 97°$
$KRuF_6$	Rhombohedral	$a = 4.86$ Å	$\alpha = 97.5°$

Rhenium Complex Chlorides

Hexachlororhenates (IV).—The hexachlororhenate (IV) ion is probably the best known and most studied complex of rhenium. It is usually made by reduction of perrhenate in hydrochloric acid using one of several possible reducing agents or alternatively by dissolving rhenium dioxide in hydrochloric acid.

The first reported preparations of potassium hexachlororhenate (IV) involved the reduction of potassium perrhenate with potassium iodide in hydrochloric acid solution.[15-18]

$$KReO_4 + 3 KI + 8 HCl \rightarrow K_2ReCl_6 + 2 KCl + 3 I + 4 H_2O$$

The reaction is considerably more complicated than the simple overall equation implies. There is very strong evidence that the first stage involves rapid reduction to Re^V followed by comparatively slow reduction to oxy and hydroxy compounds of Re^{IV} and finally complete substitution of chlorine to give potassium hexachlororhenate (IV). The gradual colour changes which occur during the rather lengthy reduction suggest that the reaction is very complex. Several oxy and hydroxy compounds which must be regarded as intermediates between the perrhenate and hexa-chlororhenate ions have actually been isolated from this reaction under varying conditions as described below. However, repeated evaporation of the reaction mixture with concentrated hydrochloric acid yields an emerald green solution of potassium hexachlororhenate which can be recovered in high yield on evaporation. Some of the earlier workers claimed that further reaction with hydrochloric acid led to further reduction to Re^{III} but this is contrary to the experience of the author and other workers.

Rulfs and Meyer[19] developed what is probably the most convenient preparation of the hexachlororhenate (IV) ion using hypophosphorus acid to reduce potassium perrhenate in hydrochloric acid solution. In a typical preparation 3 g of potassium perrhenate with 0.77 g potassium chloride in 100 ml of concentrated hydrochloric acid was reduced by 20 ml of 50% hypophosphorus acid merely by boiling till the solution was green.

Rhenium dioxide dissolves readily in concentrated hydrochloric acid to give first of all a brown solution which probably contains hydroxy-chloro complexes but on boiling the colour of the solution rapidly changes to the characteristic green of the hexachlororhenate (IV) ion and addition of potassium chloride leads to precipitation of the potassium salt. Schweitzer and Wilhelm[20] prepared their dioxide by the reduction of potassium perrhenate in alkali solution with hydrazine sulphate and used this general method to prepare the complex bromides and iodides as well as the chloride. The author has found the hydrolysis of rhenium penta-chloride a convenient source of the dioxide.

G

Potassium hexachlororhenate (IV) has a cubic lattice of the potassium hexachloroplatinate type.[21] The unit cell size is $a = 9.861 \pm 0.003$ Å with a Re–Cl distance of 2.37 ± 0.025 Å.

The magnetic properties of the hexachlororhenate (IV) ion have been the subject of several investigations. The earlier measurements[5, 22] showed that the anion obeyed the Curie–Weiss Law and some values for different cations are shown in Table 5-4.

Table 5-4. Magnetic properties of salts of hexachlororhenate (IV) ion

Complex	$\mu_{eff300°}$	θ
K_2ReCl_6	3.25	88
Cs_2ReCl_6	3.35	45
$(pyH)_2ReCl_6$	3.58	14
$(QH)_2ReCl_6$	3.54	13
$(TH)_2ReCl_6$	3.50	35

pyH^+ = pyridinium; QH^+ = quinolinium; TH^+ = toluidinium.

However, the nature of the susceptibility variations suggested that there was considerable antiferromagnetic interaction in these complexes. In an attempt to reduce the interaction the salts of large cations were prepared as shown in the Table. For the pyridinium and quinolinium salts θ is small but for the potassium and toluidinium salts it is rather high. The latter pair were shown to be isostructural but the first two showed two different structures.[22]

In another effort to make the samples more magnetically dilute Westland and Bhiwandher[23] measured the susceptibility of pure potassium hexachlororhenate (IV) and mixtures of this compound and potassium hexachloroplatinate (IV) but the results showed that significant superexchange was still occurring causing a lowering of the magnetic moment. They obtained a room temperature moment of 3.72 B.M. ($\theta = 90°$) for the pure compound and a moment of 3.76 B.M. ($\theta = 26$) for mixtures with the platinum salt.

The suggestion that these compounds are antiferromagnetic has been confirmed by recent susceptibility measurements extending down to liquid helium temperatures.[24] The Curie temperature was found to be 12.4°K and at higher temperatures they found the Curie–Weiss Law to be obeyed with $\theta = 55 \pm 5°$. The large discrepancy between this θ value and those noted above is rather curious, and suggests that perhaps some of the samples were not completely pure, but nevertheless the overall picture of the magnetic behaviour of potassium hexachlororhenate (IV) is fairly clear.

In this most recent work[24] a value for the spin-orbit coupling constant of Re^{IV} of 1460 cm^{-1} was derived which differs considerably from the values calculated by Griffiths[25] (2400 cm^{-1}) and Eisenstein[26] (2300 cm^{-1}).

The visible and infra-red spectra of potassium hexachlororhenate(IV) have been observed[27] and an unusual amount of fine structure is displayed in the electronic bands. For comparison the spectrum of hexachlororhenic acid in cyclohexane was measured, the vibrational splitting on the 7100 Å band was not enhanced, but the 10,800 Å band in the potassium salt became a doublet at 10,600 and 11,100 Å for the free acid. No peaks were observed between 12,000 and 15,000 Å.

The solubility of potassium hexachlororhenate(IV) in very dilute hydrochloric acid solutions has been found to be independent of the acid concentration. The concentration of a saturated solution was found to be 0.1664 moles/1000 g at 25° and 0.0832 moles/1000 g at 0°[28] although these values were later slightly modified to 0.1689 and 0.0841 moles/1000 g at 25° and 0° respectively.[29] The concentration of the solution was determined from its visible spectrum. The results were significantly lower than those obtained earlier by Rulfs and Meyer[19] who obtained a saturation concentration of 0.175 moles at 25° but Busey and coworkers[28, 29] suggest that Rulfs and Meyer did not obtain true equilibrium in their solutions.

The integral heat of solution of potassium hexachlororhenate(IV) in 0.0100 M hydrochloric acid solution has been measured as a function of concentration using a solution calorimeter consisting of a Dewar flask and a copper resistance thermometer.[28, 29] The results obtained are shown in Table 5-5.

Table 5-5. Heats of solution of K_2ReCl_6 in 0.01 M HCl

Heat of solution	Concentration
10,637	0.02602
10,627	0.02471
10,580	0.01197
10,535	0.00514

Extrapolation to infinite dilution gave $\Delta H_{25°} = 10,397$ cal/mole. Taking the solubility of the salt as 0.1664 mole/1000 g the entropy of $ReCl_6^{2-}$ (aq) was calculated[28] to be 59.5 ± 0.4 cal/deg/mole.

The heat capacity of solid potassium hexachlororhenate(IV) has been measured over the range 7.09–300°K.[29] The compound exhibits four cooperative transitions with maxima at 11.9°, 76.05°, 103.4° and 110.9°K, but only the one at 11.9° is associated with a magnetic transition.

Other chloro complexes of Re^{IV}.—Krauss and Dahlmann[17] claimed to have isolated green potassium hydroxypentachlororhenate(IV), $K_2[Re(OH)Cl_5]$ as one of the products of the reduction of potassium perrhenate by potassium iodide in hydrochloric acid solution. This was later confirmed by Jezowska-Trzebiatowska[18, 30] who also isolated potassium μ-oxo-decachlororhenate(IV), $K_4[Re_2OCl_{10}]$, and potassium oxopentachloro-rhenate(V), K_2ReOCl_5, as further products. It was further shown[30] that $K_2[Re(OH)Cl_5]$ and $K_4[Re_2OCl_{10}]$ are in mutual equilibrium in solution. The absorption spectrum of the reaction mixture showed that the hydroxy compound was the primary product and that it gradually changed to the binuclear species which is the more stable entity below 18°. Molar conductivity measurements confirmed the formulation as 3 and 5 ion electrolytes respectively. The mononuclear hydroxy compound had a magnetic susceptibility corresponding to three unpaired electrons but the binuclear compound had only a very small temperature-independent paramagnetism.

The crystal structure of $K_2[Re_2OCl_{10}]$ has been determined from single crystal studies.[31] It was found that the compound dehydrated at 125° losing one molecule of water. The x-ray studies showed that the compound should indeed be formulated as $K_4[Re_2OCl_{10}]\cdot H_2O$. The unit cell is tetragonal with $a = 7.070 \pm 0.004$ Å and $c = 17.719 \pm 0.005$ Å. The structure shows the presence of the $[Cl_5-Re-O-Re-Cl_5]^{4-}$ anion formed by joining of two octahedra by the common oxygen atom. The rhenium–chlorine bond distance is 2.38 Å and the rhenium–oxygen distance is 1.86 Å.

The treatment by Dunitz and Orgel[32] to explain the diamagnetism of the corresponding ruthenium compound may equally well be applied to this case.

Chloro complexes of Re^{III}.—There have been several attempts to prepare hexachlororhenate(III) salts of $ReCl_6^{3-}$, but the anion is not well established. Krauss and Dahlmann[17] claimed that potassium hexachlororhenate(III) was the ultimate reduction product of potassium perrhenate in hydrochloric acid solution, but this is not in accord with more recent work.

Manchot and Dusing[33] reduced solutions of potassium hexachloro-rhenate(IV) electrolytically using a mercury cathode. They observed that the solution first turned darker green and then brown, supposedly due to hydrolysis. It was shown that four equivalents of oxygen were absorbed on standing, thus strongly suggesting that a Re^{III} species existed in solution but no compounds were actually isolated. The same method has been used by Russian workers[34] and they claimed the isolation of caesium hexachlororhenate(III) as fine green crystals. Unfortunately the claim was not substantiated by magnetic evidence and only rhenium analyses were reported. The author has repeated these experiments[25] and obtained on addition of caesium chloride to the reduced solution, a buff precipitate, which had approximately the rhenium analysis reported by the Russians, but caesium and chlorine analyses showed that the product was not caesium hexachlororhenate (III) but rather an ill-defined mixture.

Other Russian workers[36] have claimed the preparation of the hexachlororhenate (III) ion by the hydrogenation of ammonium or potassium perrhenate in concentrated hydrochloric acid solutions at pressures of about 100 lb/in². Ammonium perrhenate gave green ammonium hexachlororhenate (IV) and yellow ammonium hexachlororhenate (III), while potassium perrhenate was said to give either blue–black potassium tetrachlororhenate (II) or a mixture of potassium hexachlororhenate (IV) and yellow potassium hexachlororhenate (III). Unfortunately again no magnetic evidence has been reported to support the claims and so the existence of the hexachlororhenate (III) ion must still be considered doubtful.

In contrast to the rather unsatisfactory state of affairs concerning the hexachlororhenate (III) ion, the structure of another chlorocomplex of tervalent rhenium has been determined with rather surprising results. It has been known for many years that rhenium trichloride is stabilized in hydrochloric acid solution and is then very difficult to oxidize.[37] It was also shown that addition of a large excess of rubidium chloride in 35% hydrochloric acid solution to a hydrochloric acid solution of rhenium trichloride led to the slow separation of a red crystalline salt, rubidium tetrachlororhenate (III), $RbReCl_4$. The salt was completely stable in air, soluble in dilute hydrochloric acid and in water giving the reactions of rhenium trichloride in solution. On heating, the salt decomposed to give a sublimate of rhenium trichloride, a black residue from which rubidium hexachlororhenate (IV) could be isolated leaving rhenium metal. The equation representing the thermal decomposition was shown to be

$$6\ RbReCl_4 \rightarrow 2\ ReCl_3 + Re + 3\ Rb_2ReCl_6$$

The caesium salt was also isolated; it behaves very similarly but it is far less soluble. The salts are diamagnetic, a phenomenon which could be explained on valence bond theory only by postulating tetrahedral d^3s hybridization.

The structure of the tetrachlororhenate(III) anion, Fig. 2, has been determined independently by two groups of investigators and it is gratifying that complete agreement within experimental error has been obtained for this unique structure.[38, 39] Caesium tetrachlororhenate was found to be orthorhombic with $a = 14.08$ Å; $b = 14.00$ Å and $c = 10.69$ Å.[39] The unit cell contains twelve molecules and the space group is $Ama2$.

The $ReCl_4^-$ anion is not tetrahedral but is trimeric with a triangle of bonded rhenium atoms (Fig. 2). Each of these is bonded to a bridging chlorine atom and one terminal chlorine atom in the plane of the triangle and also to two terminal chlorine atoms on opposite sides of this plane.

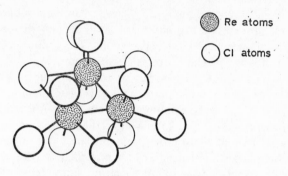

Figure 2. Structure of the tetrachlororhenate(III) ion.
(Reproduced from ROBINSON, FERGUSSON and PENFOLD. *Proc. Chem. Soc.*,
116 (1963).)

Mean values for the bond distances were found to be[38]

$$\text{Re–Re} = 2.50 \text{ Å}$$
$$\text{Re–Cl (bridging)} = 2.43 \text{ Å}$$
$$\text{Re–Cl terminal (in plane)} = 2.60 \text{ Å}$$
$$\text{Re–Cl terminal (off plane)} = 2.35 \text{ Å}$$

A molecular orbital treatment to account for the structure of the anion has been given.[39]

Chloro complexes of Re^V.—The only chlorocomplex reported for Re^V is the oxopentachlororhenate(v) ion, $ReOCl_5^{2-}$. As mentioned earlier the potassium salt is one of the products of the reduction of potassium perrhenate by potassium iodide in hydrochloric acid solution.[40] It has recently been found that salts of this anion may readily be precipitated from a solution of rhenium pentachloride freshly dissolved in concentrated hydrochloric acid solution. Addition of rubidium or caesium chlorides also in concentrated hydrochloric acid leads to the precipitation of pale buff crystalline precipitates of rubidium or caesium oxopentachlororhenates(v), $M_2(ReOCl_5)$. The salts hydrolyse in water and alkali solution to give rhenium dioxide and perrhenate ion in the ratio expected for compounds of Re^V

$$3 \text{ Re}^V \rightarrow 2 \text{ Re}^{IV} + \text{Re}^{VII}$$

The magnetic susceptibilities of the salts have been measured over a wide temperature range. The Curie–Weiss Law is strictly obeyed with small values of θ giving, perhaps rather surprisingly, a magnetic moment of 1.73 B.M.

Technetium Complex Chlorides

Hexachlorotechnates (IV).—Potassium hexachlorotechnate (IV) has been prepared by methods similar to those used to prepare the corresponding rhenium compound. It can be made by the reduction of potassium pertechnetate alone[41] but it is usual to add some potassium iodide to facilitate the reduction.[42, 43] In the latter method red crystals of an intermediate oxide halide usually separate out and these will be discussed later. Potassium hexachlorotechnate (IV) forms golden yellow octahedra and it is isostructural with the corresponding rhenate and platinate, the lattice is face-centred cubic with $a = 9.89$ Å.[42] The magnetic properties of the solid compound have been studied over a wide temperature range. It obeyed the Curie–Weiss Law with $\theta = 87°$ and an effective magnetic moment of 4.3 B.M.[42] The magnetic moment of the compound in hydrochloric acid solution has been measured twice, a value of 4.05 B.M. was obtained using the Gouy method[43] and a value of 3.83 B.M. was found[35] using the n.m.r. method.[44] In both cases measurements were made at room temperature only and the Curie Law was assumed to hold, that is $\theta = 0$. If the value of $\theta = 87°$ obtained on the solid compound is used to correct the magnetic moments in solution the value obtained by the Gouy method becomes 4.61 B.M. and by the n.m.r. method 4.36 B.M., the latter value being in excellent agreement with the value obtained on the solid. This is a good example of the usefulness of the n.m.r. method when only small amounts of material are available and the Gouy method has to be used in its least accurate form on solutions.

The hexachlorotechnate (IV) ion is not so stable as its rhenium analogue. Thus the silver salt cannot be prepared by the reaction of silver nitrate on a neutral solution of the potassium salt because of rapid hydrolysis of the complex anion, although this method can be used for preparing silver hexachlororhenate (IV). Even qualitative observation shows that potassium hexachlorotechnate (IV) is hydrolysed in dilute hydrochloric acid; a more detailed study has indicated that the potassium salt is unstable in 1 M hydrochloric acid, decomposing to an unidentified oxygenated species with the ultimate formation of pertechnetate ion.[41]

Other chlorocomplexes of technetium.—The first crystals which separate during the reduction of potassium pertechnetate by potassium iodide in hydrochloric acid are red.[35] When digested with large quantities of hydrochloric acid these dissolve to give a reddish solution, which slowly becomes light yellow and deposits crystals of hexachlorotechnate (IV) on cooling. These red crystals contain quadrivalent technetium and were thought to be potassium μ-oxodecachlorotechnate (IV), $K_4[Tc_2OCl_{10}] \cdot H_2O$, analogous to the well-known ruthenium and rhenium compounds. However, x-ray diffraction work showed the compound to have a face-centred cubic lattice instead of the tetragonal symmetry structure for the oxygen-bridged complex. It is now thought that these crystals may be the analytically identical complex potassium pentachlorohydroxytechnate(IV), $K_2TcCl_5(OH)$, which might be expected to have a cubic lattice.[40]

Chloro complexes of technetium(V) have been observed in solution.[41] In 12 M hydrochloric acid potassium pertechnetate was reduced directly to technetium(V) without the formation of detectable intermediate compounds, and it was suggested that the tetrachlorooxotechnate(V) ion, $TcOCl_4^-$, was formed although no derivatives were isolated. The absorption spectrum of the complex showed bands at 2925 and 2300 Å ($\epsilon = 4700$ and 10,400 respectively). Further reduction to hexachlorotechnate(IV) occurred only slowly. The technetium(V) complex, whilst stable in 3 M hydrochloric acid, disproportionated to pertechnetate and the hydrolysis products of hexachlorotechnate(IV) in 1 M acid.[41]

A different complex of technetium(V) was said to be produced when a solution of potassium hexachlorotechnate(V) in 12 M hydrochloric acid was exposed to sunlight.[41]

Rhenium Complex Bromides

Only one complex bromide, the hexabromorhenate(IV) ion, $ReBr_6^{2-}$, is well established although the hydroxypentabromorhenate(IV) ion $ReBr_5(OH)^{2-}$, was claimed as a product of the reduction of potassium perrhenate with hydrobromic acid and potassium bromide.[17]

Hexabromorhenic acid, H_2ReBr_6, may be prepared in solution by reduction of perrhenic acid by hydrobromic acid[45] or by dissolution of rhenium dioxide in hydrobromic acid.[20] The potassium salt is prepared by addition of potassium bromide to solutions of the acid or directly by reduction of potassium perrhenate using hypophosphorus acid in the presence of potassium bromide and hydrobromic acid[19] or by the evaporation of solid potassium hexachlororhenate(IV) with successive aliquots of hydrobromic acid.[35, 43]

Potassium hexabromorhenate(IV) is a dark red solid which is soluble in hydrobromic acid to give yellow or red solutions. It is rapidly hydrolysed, especially on warming, in water or alkali solution giving rhenium dioxide quantitatively. Its solubility in 3.0 M hydrobromic acid at 25° has been reported to be 107 g/l.[19]

The magnetic properties of potassium hexabromorhenate(IV) have been examined over a temperature range.[22] It obeys the Curie–Weiss Law with $\theta = 105°$ and $\mu_{eff} = 3.70$ B.M. The crystal lattice is face-centred cubic with $a = 10.38 \pm 0.02$ Å.[43]

The activation energy of Br^{82} exchange with the hexabromorhenate(IV) ion has been found to be 29.4 kcal/mole.[46] It was found that exposure to light, platinum tetrabromide and reducing agents such as stannous chloride, accelerated the exchange. Oxidizing agents such as bromine and potassium ferricyanide were found to be transfer inhibitors.

Technetium Complex Bromides

Only one complex bromide of technetium has so far been characterized, potassium hexabromotechnate(IV), K_2TcBr_6. The compound was prepared by treating the corresponding hexachlorotechnate(IV) with successive portions of hydrobromic acid and repeatedly evaporating the solution to expel the hydrochloric acid formed in the exchange reaction.[43]

Potassium hexabromotechnate(IV) forms dark red or black crystals which have a face-centred cubic lattice ($a = 10.37 \pm 0.02$ Å) isostructural with the corresponding bromorhenate. The compound hydrolyses very readily in water and dilute hydrobromic acid but it can be recrystallized from concentrated hydrobromic acid. The magnetic moment of the complex has only been measured in solution at room temperature, a value of 3.94 B.M. was obtained by the Gouy method[43] and 3.5 B.M. by the n.m.r. method.[35]

Rhenium Complex Iodides

Hexaiodorhenate(IV).—Potassium hexaiodorhenate(IV), K_2ReI_6, may be prepared in similar ways to the corresponding chloride and bromide. The earliest preparative method was the reduction of potassium perrhenate with hydroiodic acid and potassium iodide.[17, 47] It has also been prepared by the dissolution of rhenium dioxide in hydriodic acid followed by addition of potassium iodide,[35] by reduction of potassium perrhenate using hypophosphorus acid in the presence of hydriodic acid and potassium iodide[20] or by evaporating the corresponding complex chloride or bromide with successive aliquots of hydriodic acid.[35, 43]

Potassium hexaiodorhenate(IV) is a very dark red, or even black, solid which rapidly hydrolyses in water or alkali solution with quantitative precipitation of rhenium dioxide. It is soluble in hydriodic acid and also gives moderately stable solutions in dry methanol and acetone. Potassium hexaiodorhenate(IV) is not isostructural with the other halo complexes of this type. It has an orthorhombic unit cell with the following dimensions[48]

$$a = 11.07 \pm 0.05 \text{ Å}$$
$$b = 13.48 \pm 0.07 \text{ Å}$$
$$c = 10.19 \pm 0.05 \text{ Å}$$

The magnetic moment for the compound has been found to be 3.32 B.M. at 300°K with $\theta = 100°$.[22]

Other iodo complexes of Re^{IV}.—Biltz and coworkers[49] observed that when potassium hexaiodorhenate(IV) was dissolved in 20% sulphuric acid solution the red colour could be extracted with ether. Furthermore it was shown that all the potassium and one-sixth of the iodine remained in the aqueous phase and that all the rhenium and five-sixths of the iodine was extracted into the ether layer. It was also shown that the rhenium was still in the tetravalent state. On the basis of these observations they suggested that the following reaction occurred

$$K_2ReI_6 + H_2SO_4 \rightarrow K_2SO_4 + HI + HReI_5$$

but neither the complex acid nor its salts were isolated.

These observations have recently been confirmed and by addition of an alcoholic solution of tetraethylammonium chloride to the ether solution of the complex rhenium acid a salt has been isolated and shown to be tetraethylammonium hydroxypentaiodorhenate(IV), $[N(C_2H_5)_4]_2[ReI_5OH]$.[50] Thus it becomes apparent that in 20% sulphuric acid potassium hexaiodorhenate(IV) is extensively hydrolysed to the hydroxypentaiodo complex. That this is correct has been substantiated by the observation that in (1 + 1) sulphuric acid solution the extraction by ether does not occur, presumably because the hydrolysis is suppressed and the hexaiodorhenate(IV) ion has no way of forming a hydrogen bond to the ether for extraction to occur. Biltz also observed that under the same conditions the corresponding complex bromide did not extract into ether. This has also been confirmed, but it has been found that if the bromo complex is dissolved in very dilute alkali solution and allowed to stand for a few minutes hydrolysis does occur since on acidification and shaking with ether partial extraction occurs. The fact that alkali conditions are required for hydrolysis merely reflects the rather greater stability of the complex bromide to hydrolysis compared with the iodide.

Technetium Complex Iodides

Only one complex iodide of technetium has been characterized, potassium hexaiodotechnate(IV), K_2TcI_6. It is prepared by digesting either the corresponding chloro- or bromotechnates with successive portions of hydriodic acid.[43] The shining black crystals give an x-ray diffraction pattern almost identical with that of potassium hexaiodorhenate(IV) and it is not isostructural with the chloro- and bromotechnates. Morrow[48] has reported that the hexaiodorhenate(IV) has orthorhombic symmetry with four formula weights in the unit cell but Dalziel and coworkers found that most of the lines could be indexed more satisfactorily with respect to a body-centred orthorhombic cell which contained two formula weights. The x-ray diffraction data for potassium hexaiodotechnate (IV) has been interpreted in the same way giving a unit cell of the following dimensions: $a = 11.22$ Å; $b = 8.00$ Å and $c = 7.84$ Å with an error of $\pm$ 0.03 Å along each axis.[43]

The magnetic moment of potassium hexaiodotechnate (IV) has been found to be 4.14 B.M. the measurements were made in hydriodic acid solution by the Gouy method and the Curie Law was assumed to hold.[43]

References

1. O. Ruff and W. Kwasnik, *Z. Anorg. Allgem. Chem.* **219**, 65 (1934).
2. E. Weise, *Z. Anorg. Allgem. Chem.* **283**, 377 (1956).
3. R. D. Peacock, *Chem. Ind. London* 1453 (1955).
4. R. D. Peacock, *J. Chem. Soc.* 1291 (1956).
5. B. N. Figgis, J. Lewis and F. E. Mabbs, *J. Chem. Soc.* 3138 (1961).
6. R. D. Peacock, *J. Chem. Soc.* 467 (1957).
7. G. B. Hargreaves and R. D. Peacock, *J. Chem. Soc.* 3776 (1958).
8. N. S. Nikolaev and E. G. Ippolitov, *Dokl. Akad. Nauk SSSR* **136**, 111 (1961).
9. N. S. Nikolaev and E. G. Ippolitov, *Dokl. Akad. Nauk SSSR* **140**, 129 (1961).
10. E. G. Ippolitov, *Zh. Neorgan. Khim.* **7**, 940 (1962).
11. R. D. Peacock, *J. Chem. Soc.* 602 (1955).
12. G. E. Boyd, Personal communication quoted by R. Colton and R. D. Peacock, *Quart. Rev. London* **16**, 299 (1962).
13. K. Schwochau and W. Herr, *Angew. Chem. Intern. Ed. Engl.* **2**, 97 (1963).
14. A. J. Edwards, D. Hugill and R. D. Peacock, *Nature* **200**, 672 (1963).
15. E. Enk, *Chem. Ber.* **64B**, 791 (1931).
16. F. Krauss and H. Steinfeld, *Chem. Ber.* **64B**, 2552 (1931).
17. F. Krauss and H. Dahlmann, *Chem. Ber.* **65B**, 877 (1932).
18. B. Jezowska-Trzebiatowska, *Trav. Soc. Sci. Lettres Wroclaw, Ser. B* **39**, 5 (1953).
19. C. L. Rulfs and R. J. Meyer, *J. Am. Chem. Soc.* **77**, 4505 (1955).
20. G. K. Schweitzer and D. L. Wilhelm, *J. Inorg. Nucl. Chem.* **3**, 1 (1956).
21. B. Aminoff, *Z. Krist.* **94**, 246 (1936).
22. B. N. Figgis, J. Lewis, R. S. Nyholm and R. D. Peacock, *Discussions Faraday Soc.* **26**, 103 (1958).
23. A. D. Westland and N. C. Bhiwandher, *Can. J. Chem.* **39**, 1284 (1961).
24. R. H. Busey and E. H. Sondar, *J. Chem. Phys.* **36**, 93 (1962).
25. J. H. E. Griffiths, J. Owen and I. M. Ward, *Proc. Roy. Soc. London Ser. A.* **219**, 526 (1953).
26. J. C. Eisenstein, *J. Chem. Phys.* **34**, 1628 (1961).
27. R. H. Busey, *Unclassified Document* O.R.N.L. 2983 (1961).
28. R. H. Busey and R. B. Bevan, Jnr., *Unclassified Document* O.R.N.L. 2983 (1961).

29. R. H. Busey, H. H. Dearman and R. B. Bevan, Jnr., *J. Phys. Chem.* **66**, 82 (1962).
30. B. Jezowska-Trzebiatowska and S. Wajda, *Bull. Acad. Polon. Sci. Classe III* **2**, 249 (1954).
31. J. C. Morrow, *Acta Cryst.* **15**, 851 (1962).
32. J. D. Dunitz and L. E. Orgel, *J. Chem. Soc.* 2594 (1953).
33. W. Manchot and J. Dusing, *Z. Anorg. Allgem. Chem.* **212**, 21 (1933).
34. D. I. Ryabchikov, V. A. Zarinskii and I. I. Nazarenko, *Zh. Neorgan. Khim.* **6**, 1138 (1961).
35. R. Colton, Unpublished observations.
36. V. G. Tronev and S. M. Bondin, *Khim. Redkikh Elementov Akad. Nauk SSR Inst. Obshch. i Neorgan. Khim.* **1**, 40 (1954).
37. W. Geilmann and F. W. Wrigge, *Z. Anorg. Allgem. Chem.* **233**, 144 (1935).
38. W. T. Robinson, J. E. Fergusson and B. L. Penfold, *Proc. Chem. Soc.* 116, (1963).
39. J. A. Bertrand, F. A. Cotton and W. A. Dollase, *J. Am. Chem. Soc.* **85**, 1349 (1963).
40. D. Brown and R. Colton, to be published.
41. R. H. Busey, *Unclassified Document* O.R.N.L. 2782 (1959).
42. C. M. Nelson, G. E. Boyd and W. T. Smith, Jnr., *J. Am. Chem. Soc.* **76**, 348 (1954).
43. J. Dalziel, N. S. Gill, R. S. Nyholm and R. D. Peacock, *J. Chem. Soc.* 4012 (1958).
44. D. F. Evans, *J. Chem. Soc.* 2003 (1959).
45. R. Colton and G. Wilkinson, *Chem. Ind. London* 1314 (1959).
46. G. Schmidt and W. Herr, *Z. Naturforsch* **16a**, 748 (1961).
47. H. V. A. Briscoe, P. L. Robinson and A. J. Rudge, *J. Chem. Soc.* 3218 (1931).
48. J. C. Morrow, *J. Phys. Chem.* **60**, 19 (1956).
49. W. Biltz, F. W. Wrigge, E. Prange and G. Lange, *Z. Anorg. Allgem. Chem.* **234**, 142 (1933).
50. R. Colton, *Aust. J. Chem.*, **18**, 435 (1965).

6

Complex Compounds

A considerable number of complexes derived from rhenium halides have been prepared using organic groups as ligands. As might be expected not many examples of this type of compound have yet been prepared for technetium, the only ones so far reported are some ditertiary arsine complexes. A wide range of oxidation states of rhenium are represented in these compounds and for convenience they will be treated in sections according to whether the organic groups are nitrogen, phosphorus, arsenic, oxygen or sulphur ligands.

Nitrogen Ligands

The action of anhydrous gaseous ammonia on dry rhenium trichloride at 3–5 atmospheres pressure for 6 hours yielded a voluminous black powder.[1] Adsorbed ammonia was removed by pumping until the sample attained constant weight. Analysis showed the material to be tetrammine rhenium trichloride, $[Re(NH_3)_4]Cl_3$. Experiments showed that all of the chlorine was ionic and could be precipitated by silver nitrate. The thermal decomposition of the tetrammine was said to give $[Re(NH_3)_2(NH_2)_2]Cl$ and prolonged heating gave a product which approximated to rhenium nitride Re_2N.[1]

Two complexes of quadrivalent rhenium with pyridine are known, bis(pyridine) rhenium tetrachloride and bis(pyridine) rhenium tetraiodide. Two preparations of bis(pyridine) rhenium tetrachloride, py_2ReCl_4, have been reported, firstly[2] by the thermal decomposition of pyridinium hexachlororhenate (IV), $(pyH)_2ReCl_6$, at 300° and more recently[3] by the action of pyridine in a sealed tube at 200° on either pyridinium or potassium hexachlororhenate (IV). The compound is insoluble in water and is a non-electrolyte in organic solvents,[2] its magnetic moment is given as 3.3 B.M.

Bis(pyridine) rhenium tetraiodide has been prepared by the direct inter-action of acetone solutions of pyridine and rhenium tetraiodide.[4, 5] The brown complex crystallized out quickly and was washed with acetone and ether. The magnetic moment at room temperature (assuming $\theta = 0$) was 3.7 B.M.

Pyridine forms several complexes with rhenium trichloride. By addition of pyridine to an acetone solution of the trichloride a red solution con-taining some bis(pyridine) rhenium trichloride was obtained.[5] This com-plex could be precipitated by addition of ether to the solution but some un-reacted rhenium trichloride invariably precipitated also, preventing positive identification of the complex. However, its properties were very similar to those of other complexes of this type which will be described later in this section. The acetone solution of rhenium trichloride and pyridine turned green on standing for some time, or more quickly on heating, and from this green solution sparingly soluble pyridine rhenium trichloride, $pyReCl_3$, was precipitated by addition of ether.[5] By the action of pyridine on rhenium trichloride in an autoclave at 200° for 3–4 hours at 15–20 atmospheres pressure yellow tetrapyridine rhenium trichloride was obtained[2] in a similar manner to tetrammine rhenium trichloride.

It has been claimed[6] that the calculated amount of pyridine reacts with ammonium tetrachlororhenate (II) to give bis(pyridine) rhenium di-chloride, $(py)_2ReCl_2$ in the form of the *cis* isomer. The *trans* isomer was prepared by heating tetrapyridine rhenium dichloride $(py)_4ReCl_2$ with hydrochloric acid.

$$Re(py)_4Cl_2 + 2\,HCl \rightarrow trans\text{-}Re(py)_2Cl_2 + 2\,pyHCl$$

This work is particularly interesting as it implies that divalent rhenium can form square planar complexes, the only other known examples of divalent rhenium are octahedral. Unfortunately the results were not supported by magnetic work and some doubt must remain about the authenticity of these complexes until they are confirmed.

A remarkable series of complexes has been claimed to result from the interaction of pyridine and an aqueous solution of potassium hexa-chlororhenate (IV).[7] The first product was said to be tetrapyridine rhenium dioxide dichloride, $ReO_2Cl_2(py)_4$, which crystallized out as a red solid. From the mother liquor the yellow crystalline compound $[ReO_2(py)_4]I$ was obtained by addition of potassium iodide solution. On further standing of the mother liquors other complexes said to be $Re_2O_5 \cdot (py)_5$ and $[ReO_2(py)_4]Cl$ were obtained. This latter compound has also been pre-pared by the action of pyridine on tetrachlororhenates (II) and evaporating the solution exposed to the air.[8] The corresponding ethylenediamine complex is well known and is described below.

The synthesis of tetrakis(ethylamine) rhenium trichloride and tetrakis-(diethylamine) rhenium trichloride, which are formally analogous to tetrammine rhenium trichloride have been reported.[2] Rhenium trichloride was dissolved in ethylamine, the solution was initially red but rapidly became brown. After 10 hours the excess ethylamine was removed under vacuum and the remaining black solid was dried at 40° under vacuum. Analysis showed the compound to be $ReCl_3(C_2H_5NH_2)_4$. The complex was readily hydrolysed by water but it dissolved without apparent decomposition in alcohol and acetone to give brown solutions. This method of preparation was not successful for the diethylamine complex which had to be prepared by the autoclave method described earlier.[2]

Rhenium trichloride reacts with more complicated nitrogen ligands to give polymeric complexes. With 1,10-phenanthroline and 2,2'-dipyridyl highly insoluble and presumably polymeric products of stoichiometry Re_2Cl_4L were obtained by direct interaction in acetone solution.[5] On mixing solutions of rhenium trichloride with a solution of the ligand in acetone a purple diamagnetic precipitate formed almost immediately. The simplest structure unit, since the two nitrogens must occupy *cis* positions is structure A. Polymeric structures giving octahedral configuration of the rhenium, possibly with metal–metal bonding, are also possible.

Structure A

In any formulation rhenium atoms in both (II) and (III) oxidation states must be present. It is well known that compounds containing mixed valency states are highly coloured and these complexes are deep purple.

When suspended in acetone these complexes are smoothly oxidized by chlorine to give a red solution from which complexes of the type $ReCl_3L$ were precipitated by addition of ether. These complexes were diamagnetic, non-conductors in nitrobenzene and appear to be true 5-coordinate species. They are very soluble in alcohol and moderately soluble in acetone, chloroform and nitrobenzene.[5]

With quinoldine a purple complex with stoichiometry $Re_2Cl_5(quin)$ was obtained.[5] The compound was insoluble in water and appeared to contain no ionic chlorine. The complex was paramagnetic with a room temperature susceptibility of 600×10^{-6} c.g.s. giving a magnetic moment of 1.2 B.M., assuming $\theta = 0°$. The structural unit may be structure B, but again polymeric forms are likely.

$$\begin{array}{ccc}
\text{Cl} & \text{Cl} & \text{Cl} \\
\backslash & \diagup\,\backslash & \diagup \\
& \text{Re} \qquad \text{Re} \\
\diagup & \backslash\,\diagup & \backslash \\
\text{Cl} & \text{Cl} & \text{quin}
\end{array}$$

Structure B

Other amines gave complexes of the types $Re_2Cl_6L_2$ (with α-picoline) and Re_2Cl_6L (with 2,6-lutidine, 2-vinylpyridine and triethylenetetramine).[5] These were very slightly soluble in water and contained ionic chlorine, but the fraction of ionizable chlorine was not easy to determine since the cation hydrolysed rapidly to hydrated rhenium (III) oxide. As a result only total chlorine was determined.

Ethylenediamine forms an interesting series of complexes with pentavalent rhenium.[9, 10] A large excess of ethylenediamine reacted with an aqueous solution of potassium hexachlororhenate (IV) to give a complex of rhenium (V), $[ReO_2(en)_2]Cl$, which was isolated as its chloroplatinate.[9] This complex reacted with hydrochloric acid to give first a monohydroxy complex and with excess acid a dihydroxy species was formed. Treatment with alkali reversed the reactions.

$$[ReO_2(en)_2]Cl \underset{\text{NaOH}}{\overset{\text{HCl}}{\rightleftharpoons}} [ReO(OH)(en)_2]Cl_2 \underset{\text{NaOH}}{\overset{\text{HCl}}{\rightleftharpoons}} [Re(OH)_2(en)_2]Cl_3$$

blue-green   reddish-violet   blue

The monohydroxy complex is best prepared by careful addition of hydrochloric acid to a solution of the dioxo complex until the solution turns red; this complex is also best isolated as its chloroplatinate. The dihydroxy complex is made by addition of further amounts of hydrochloric acid and warming the solution to about 50° until the colour changes to blue.

Phosphorus Ligands

Phosphine complexes of rhenium have only been prepared for the first time in the last few years. However, the field has expanded so rapidly that rhenium is now known to form more types of phosphine complexes than most other metals.

The first report that rhenium forms phosphine complexes was given by Freni and Valenti.[11] They found that by using perrhenic acid and triphenylphosphine as starting materials, reaction with hydrohalic acids produced directly compounds of the type $Re(PPh_3)_2Cl_3$ with hydrochloric acid and compounds of the types $Re(PPh_3)_2Br_2$ and $Re(PPh_3)_2I_2$ with hydrobromic and hydriodic acids respectively. Unfortunately it has since been shown that all of these formulae are incorrect.[12, 13, 14] The compound formulated as $Re(PPh_3)_2Cl_3$ is in fact $ReOCl_3(PPh_3)_2$, a complex of the unknown rhenium oxide trichloride. The bromo and iodo compounds are in fact oxoalkoxide complexes of the type $[ReO(OEt)X_2(PPh_3)_2]$. The phenomenon of forming alkoxide groups from the alcohol is very unusual but it appears to be a very general property of rhenium as shown by some of the compounds listed in Table 6-1.

The complexes of triphenylphosphine are fairly insoluble in most solvents so Chatt and Rowe[14] investigated also the complexes of diethylphenylphosphine, tertiary aliphatic phosphines and some ditertiary phosphines. Three principal types of reaction were used to prepare the compounds.

Reaction 1. Interaction of alkali perrhenate or rhenium heptaoxide with the phosphine in concentrated hydrochloric acid and ethanol.

Reaction 2. Interaction of rhenium heptaoxide, the phosphine and hydrazine hydrochloride in ethanol.

Reaction 3. Interaction of rhenium trichloride with the tertiary phosphine in alcohol or acetone.

The numbering of the compounds in the following section follows that in the paper by Chatt and Rowe.[14]

With diethylphenylphosphine refluxing for several hours under the conditions of reaction 1, gave a mixture of three components, one blue (I), one green (II) and one violet (III). All three gave analyses and molecular weights corresponding to $[ReOCl_3(PEt_2Ph)_2]$. However, the violet component has since been shown[15] to be a mixture of (II) and a new complex $[ReCl_4(PEt_2Ph)_2]$ which will be discussed later. There are three possible octahedral isomers of $[ReOCl_3(PEt_2Ph)_2]$, two *cis* isomers and one *trans* isomer. The blue complex (I) is a *cis* isomer as shown by its high dipole moment of 10.8 D. The green complex (II) is the *trans* isomer as shown by its low dipole moment of 1.7 D. and this has been confirmed by a full x-ray structure determination.[16] The monoclinic crystals have a unit cell of the following dimensions: $a = 13.05 \pm 0.02$, $b = 7.83 \pm 0.01$, $c = 23.90 \pm 0.03$ Å, $\beta = 91.5 \pm 0.1°$. There are four formula units per unit cell and the space group is $P2_1/C(C_{2h}^5$ No.14). There is some distortion from true octahedral symmetry about the rhenium atom. Rather interestingly, the rhenium–phosphorus distance is normal with no evidence of $d\pi$–$d\pi$ double bonding.

Complexes (I) and (II) both gave $[ReCl_3(PEt_2Ph)_2]$ (IV) on boiling in ethanolic solution with excess of the phosphine. On boiling in ethanol

H

alone complexes (I) and (II) gave a diamagnetic complex [ReO(OR)Cl$_2$ (PEt$_2$Ph)$_2$] (V, R = Et), this reaction was general and corresponding complexes were obtained for methyl, benzyl and 2-methoxyethyl alcohol.

With triphenylphosphine only one isomer of ReOCl$_3$(PPh$_3$)$_2$ was obtained by reaction 1.[14] This was a yellow compound (XI) m.p. 220° (decomp.) having a small dipole moment of 2.5 D. and it is almost certainly the *trans* isomer corresponding to the green complex (II) for diethylphenylphosphine. Using concentrated hydrobromic or hydriodic acids instead of hydrochloric acid grey diamagnetic oxoethoxy complexes were obtained [Re(OEt)X$_2$(PPh$_3$)$_2$] (XVIII). The iodo complex (XVIII) also resulted from the reaction of potassium hexaiodorhenate(IV) with the phosphine in acetone. In this case the product was recrystallized from a benzene–ethanol mixture. If reaction 1 is carried out in propan-1-ol with hydriodic acid the substance [ReO(OPr^n)I$_2$(PPh$_3$)$_2$] (XVI) was obtained. This compound and [ReO(OEt)I$_2$(PPh$_3$)$_2$] both reacted with 2-methoxy-ethanol to give [ReO(OC$_2$H$_4$OMe)I$_2$(PPh$_3$)$_2$] (XV) showing the very ready exchange of the alkoxy groups.[14]

Under the conditions of reaction 2 no complex was formed when water was present, but in the absence of water the red complex [ReCl$_2$(PPh$_3$)$_2$] (XIII) was obtained. Reaction with sodium iodide gave the corresponding iodocomplex [ReI$_2$(PPh$_3$)$_2$]. These compounds were quite different to those given these formulae by Freni and Valenti.[11]

The aliphatic phosphines react slowly under the conditions of reaction 1, and the complexes of Re^V derived from these phosphines have been prepared by ligand exchange reactions.[15] Thus [ReOCl$_3$(PPh$_3$)$_2$] reacts with triethylphosphine to give [ReOCl$_3$(PEt$_3$)$_2$].

Many other complexes of these types have been prepared by similar reactions and some of them are listed in Table 6-1.

Phosphine complexes of Re^{IV} of the type [ReX$_4$(PR$_3$)$_2$] (X = Cl, Br or I) have also been prepared. The bromo and iodo compounds can be prepared by direct interaction of the tetrahalides and triphenylphosphine in acetone solutions,[4] but most of these compounds have been prepared by pyrolysis of the phosphonium salts of the hexahalorhenates(IV).[15] Thus [ReBr$_4$ (PEt$_2$Ph)$_2$] has been obtained by the pyrolysis of [PHEt$_2$Ph]$_2$[ReBr$_6$] which was itself prepared by the interaction of diethylphenylphosphonium bromide on potassium hexabromorhenate(IV) in hydrobromic acid.[15]

[ReCl$_4$(PPh$_3$)$_2$] was obtained by reducing *trans*-[ReOCl$_3$(PPh$_3$)$_2$] by titanous chloride in hydrochloric acid solution. Treatment of [ReCl$_4$(PPh$_3$)$_2$] with excess diethylphenylphosphine in boiling benzene gave *trans*-[ReCl$_4$(PEt$_2$Ph)$_2$]. This latter compound is monomeric in benzene solution, a non-conductor in nitrobenzene and the solid is paramagnetic with an effective magnetic moment of 3.64 B.M. at 20°.[15]

Table 6-1. Phosphine complexes of Re^V; Re^{III}, and Re^{II}

Compound	Colour	M.p. (decomp.)	$\nu Re=O$	Dipole (D.)	Ref.
Oxo complexes of Re^V					
cis-[ReOCl₃(PEt₂Ph)₂]	blue	157–160	977	10.8	13, 14
trans-[ReOCl₃(PEt₂Ph)₂]	green	166–169	978	1.7	13, 14
cis-[ReOI₃(PEt₂Ph)₂]	brown	171.5–174	976	—	14
[ReO(SCN)₃(PEt₂Ph)₂]	brown	138–142	964	—	13, 14
trans-[ReOCl₃(PPh₃)₂]	yellow	211–214	969	2.2	13, 14
trans-[ReOBr₃(PPh₃)₂]	yellow	181–183	980	—	14
[ReO(SCH)₃(PPh₃)₂]	brown	132–136	958	—	14
cis-[ReOCl₃(PEt₃)₂]	blue	126–129	982	—	13, 14, 15
trans-[ReOCl₃(PEt₃)₂]	green	164–174	973	—	13, 14, 15
[ReOCl₃ {P(CH₂Cl)₃}₂]	red	156–161	975	—	14
[ReOCl₃ {C₂H₄(PEt₂)}₂]	blue	240–243	984	—	14
oxoalkoxy complexes of Re^V					
[ReO(OMe)Cl₂(PEt₂Ph)₂]	violet	132–136	937	—	14
[ReO(OEt)Cl₂(PEt₂Ph)₂]	violet	125–139	951	—	14
[ReO(OMe)Cl₂(PPh₃)₂]	grey	200–203	946	—	13, 14
[ReO(OEt)Cl₂(PPh₃)₂]	grey	199–203	946	—	13, 14
[ReP(OEt)Br₂(PPh₃)₂]	grey-brown	147–149	940	—	13, 14
[ReO(OEt)I₂(PPh₃)₂]	green	155–165	946	—	13, 14
[ReO(OPrⁿ)I₂(PPh₃)₂]	olive-green	150–160	921	—	14
[ReO(OEt)Cl₂(PEtPh₂)₂]	purple	163–167	942	—	14
complexes of Re^{III}					
[ReCl₃(PEt₂Ph)]ₙ	purple	7350	—	—	14
ReCl₃(PEt₂Ph)₃	orange	163–166	—	—	14
(ReCl₃PPh₃)ₙ	purple	208–210	—	—	14
[ReCl₂ {C₂H₄(PPh₂)}₂]Cl	yellow	219–220	—	—	14
complexes of Re^{II}					
ReCl₂(PPh₃)₂	brick-red	219–221	—	—	14
ReI₂(PPh₃)₂	reddish-brown	178–180	—	—	14

Rhenium phosphine hydrides have been claimed[18] but in view of the fact that the starting materials were wrongly formulated there must be some doubt of the validity of the results. Starting from the supposed [Re(PPh₃)₂X₂] compounds, actually [ReO(OEt)X₂(PPh₃)₂], reduction with sodium borohydride in alcohol solution gave red crystalline ReH₃ (PPh₃)₂·2C₂H₅OH. It may well be that in this compound there are actually two alkoxide groups. Recrystallization from benzene was said to give [ReH₃(PPh₃)₂] which reacted with more triphenylphosphine to give ReH₃(PPh₃)₄.

Arsenic Ligands

Rhenium complexes.—A series of complex compounds with both rhenium

and technetium has been isolated using the bidentate arsenic ligand
o-phenylenebisdimethylarsine.

$$
\begin{array}{c}
CH_3 \quad CH_3 \\
\diagdown \diagup \\
\text{—As} \diagdown \\
\text{—As} \diagup \\
\diagup \diagdown \\
CH_3 \quad CH_3
\end{array}
$$

In the formulae of the compounds given below the symbol D will be used
to represent this ligand.

The first complexes to be prepared were those of rhenium (III) and
rhenium (II).[18] The tervalent chloro and bromo complexes were prepared
by refluxing perrhenic acid, hypophosphorus acid, the arsine and the
appropriate halogen acid in alcohol. Since perrhenic acid, hypophosphorus acid and a halogen acid leads to the formation of hexahalorhenates (IV) this method is equivalent to refluxing the arsine with a
hexahalorhenate (IV). The direct method of reaction with the hexahalo-
technate (IV) was later used for technetium. The compounds were isolated as
their sparingly soluble perchlorates which were found to be $[ReD_2Cl_2]ClO_4$
and $[ReD_2Br_2]ClO_4$. The corresponding iodide was prepared from the
bromide by displacement by iodide ion.

Neutral complexes of rhenium (II) of the type $[ReD_2Cl_2]^0$ were prepared
by vigorous reduction of the tervalent complexes with reagents such as
sodium stannite. Treatment of the divalent complexes with one equivalent
of an oxidizing agent such as ceric sulphate regenerated the tervalent
complexes.

Further oxidation of the rhenium (III) complexes with chlorine or bromine in the presence of excess diarsine gave 8-coordinate complexes of
rhenium (V) of the type $[ReD_2Cl_4]^+$ which could be also isolated as perchlorates.[19] Two equivalents of reducing agents reacted with the complexes
of rhenium (V) to give the tervalent complexes described above and these
in turn could be oxidized with two equivalents of ceric sulphate to the
rhenium (V) compounds. These reactions are diagrammatically represented
in the scheme below and some properties of these compounds are given in
Table 6-2.

The magnetic moments of the rhenium (III) complexes have also been
measured by other workers[20] who obtained almost the same values as
quoted above but they found that spin–orbit coupling is so great that the
magnetic moment is effectively temperature independent. The rhenium (II)
complexes were the first complexes of the metal in this oxidation state to

be well characterized. The molar conductivities for the tervalent complexes were higher than expected for a uni-equivalent electrolyte, usual values for the molar conductivity of such compounds in nitromethane are 70–90 Ω^{-1}.

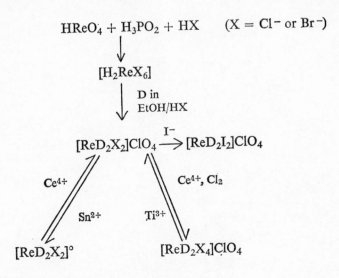

Table 6-2. Ditertiary arsine compounds of rhenium

	Compound	Colour	Molar cond. in $CH_3NO_2.1 \times 10^{-3}$ M (Ω^{-1})	Magnetic moment (B.M.)
$Re^{II}d^5$	$[ReD_2Cl_2]^\circ$ $[ReD_2Br_2]^\circ$ $[ReD_2I_2]^\circ$	yellow-brown green green	insoluble in $CH_3 \cdot NO_2$ oxidised in $C_6H_5 \cdot NO_2$	1.7–1.8
$Re^{III}d^4$	$[ReD_2Cl_2]ClO_4$ $[ReD_2Br_2]ClO_4$ $[ReD_2I_2]ClO_4$	golden-yellow orange red	113 110 118	2.1 1.99 1.8
Re^Vd^2	$[ReD_2Cl_4]ClO_4$ $[ReD_2Br_4]Br$	purple green	actual values not reported, but results said to be correct for uni-univalent electrolyte	diamagnetic

Technetium complexes.—A remarkable demonstration of how much preparative work can be achieved using small amounts of technetium has been given by Fergusson and Nyholm.[21, 22] By the use of carefully selected quantitative reactions they were able to prepare most of the technetium analogues of these rhenium complexes using only 15 mg of technetium. The reaction schemes are shown below

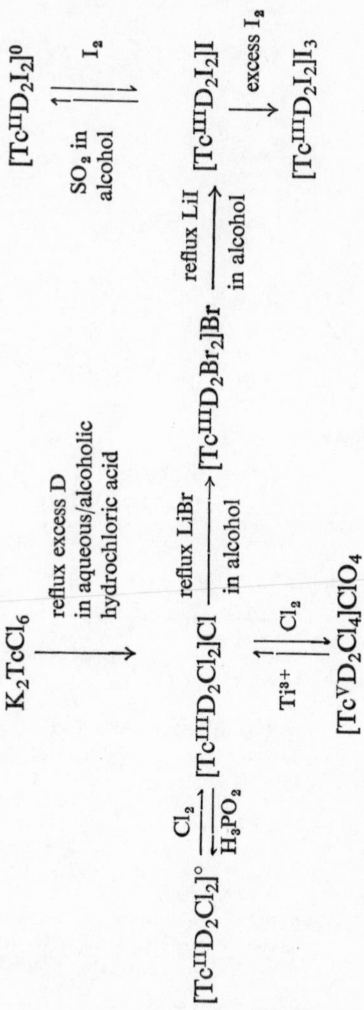

$[Tc^{II}D_2I_2]^0 \underset{I_2}{\overset{SO_2 \text{ in}}{\rightleftarrows}} [Tc^{III}D_2I_2]I \xrightarrow{\text{excess } I_2} [Tc^{III}D_2I_2]I_3$

(SO₂ in alcohol)

$[Tc^{III}D_2Br_2]Br \xrightarrow[\text{in alcohol}]{\text{reflux LiI}} [Tc^{III}D_2I_2]I$

$K_2TcCl_6 \xrightarrow[\substack{\text{in aqueous/alcoholic}\\ \text{hydrochloric acid}}]{\text{reflux excess D}} [Tc^{III}D_2Cl_2]Cl \xrightarrow[\text{in alcohol}]{\text{reflux LiBr}} [Tc^{III}D_2Br_2]Br$

$[Tc^{II}D_2Cl_2]^0 \underset{H_3PO_2}{\overset{Cl_2}{\rightleftarrows}} [Tc^{III}D_2Cl_2]Cl$

$Ti^{3+} \updownarrow Cl_2$

$[Tc^VD_2Cl_4]ClO_4$

No analyses were performed because of the small amounts of material available, but the compounds were all isomorphous with the corresponding rhenium complexes. Some properties of the technetium compounds are given in Table 6-3.

Table 6-3. Ditertiary arsine complexes of technetium

Compound		Colour	Molar. cond. in CH$_3$NO$_2$.1 $\times$ 10^{-3} M (Ω^{-1})	Magnetic moment (B.M.)
Tc^{II}d^5	[TcD$_2$Cl$_2$]^0 [TcD$_2$Br$_2$]^0 [TcD$_2$I$_2$]^0	brown	non-electrolytes	1.9–2.1
Tc^{III}d^4	[TcD$_2$Cl$_2$]Cl [TcD$_2$Br$_2$]Br [TcD$_2$I$_2$.I$_3$	orange red deep red or black	75 77 86	2.7 3.2 3.4
Tc^{V}d^2	[TcD$_2$Cl$_4$]ClO$_4$	brown		0.9 (temperature independent)

Oxygen Ligands

Complexes with oxygen ligands are known for rhenium (III), rhenium (IV) and rhenium (V).

Acetylacetone reacts with rhenium dioxide on refluxing for 48 hours to give a brown solution from which rhenium trisacetylacetonate could be precipitated by addition of ether.[5] The compound was purified by repeatedly dissolving it in acetone and precipitating with ether. Rhenium trisacetylacetonate is monomeric in solution and its magnetic susceptibility obeys the Curie–Weiss Law with $\theta = 160°$ and $\mu = 2.80$ B.M.

When solutions of rhenium trichloride in the lower carboxylic acids were heated in a nitrogen atmosphere they gradually turned from red to dark brown and diamagnetic orange crystals separated.[23] For acetic, proprionic, n and isobutyric and octanoic acids the crystals were similar and of stoichiometry [ReCl(O·COR)$_2$]$_2$. The acetate was only sparingly soluble in organic solvents, but the solubilities increased with the length of the alkyl chain so that the octanate was readily soluble in many solvents. The soluble compounds were all dimeric. All of these complexes are stable indefinitely in the air, they are unaffected by dilute mineral acids but hot alkali solutions cause hydrolysis.

These compounds are thought to contain four bridging carboxylato groups, rather than bridging chlorine groups, for several reasons. By treatment of the butyrates in benzene with silver thiocyanate the compound [Re(NCS)(O·CO·C$_3$H)$_2$]$_2$ may be isolated and the infra-red spectrum of this compound definitely suggests that the thiocyanate group is a terminal group rather than a bridging group. Similarly the complexes soluble in aqueous acetone react with silver perchlorate or sulphate to give silver chloride and a blue solution. On using the butyrate, a sparingly water-soluble sulphate $[Re(H_2O)(O \cdot CO \cdot C_3H_7)_2]_2SO_4$, was isolated. In addition to the usual bands due to acetate in the infra-red it showed strong absorptions due to coordinated water at 3400 and 1625 cm^{-1} and sulphate. This shows that the terminal chlorine atoms can be replaced by water molecules, to give a dipositive cation in which the carboxylate bridges are retained. Finally the complexes did not react with pyridine, p-toluidine or triphenylphosphine which itself strongly suggests that the compounds are not chlorine bridged.

From the dark brown solutions remaining after separation of the orange complexes, brown solids of stoichiometry $(R \cdot CO_2H)_2ReCl_3$ could be isolated. These were soluble in polar solvents, the solutions in acetone and nitrobenzene were non-conducting and molecular weights indicated monomeric species. These complexes were also diamagnetic and are regarded as true 5-coordinate species.

Different products were obtained when the trichloride was reacted with the carboxylic acid in the presence of air.[23] The initial red solutions turned orange and purple crystals separated out. For the higher acids an orange compound can be isolated from the remaining solution, but for acetic and proprionic acids the solubilities of the two complexes were so similar that separation was impossible. The purple complexes of the higher acids were of the type $[ReOCl(O \cdot COR)]_2$ and the orange compounds were of the type $[ReO_2(O \cdot COR)]_2$.

The purple oxochloro complexes were dimeric and diamagnetic and gave non-conducting solutions in acetone. The structure is thought to contain both oxo- and carboxylato-bridging groups

Evidence for the bridging oxo groups was obtained from protonation experiments. The complexes dissolved in aqueous air-free mineral acids to give blue solutions. Reaction of the isobutyrate yielded a water-in-soluble complex [Re(OH)Cl$_2$(O·CO·C$_3$H$_7$)]$_2$ which was diamagnetic, gave non-conducting solutions in nitrobenzene and showed a strong O–H stretching frequency at 3380 cm^{-1}. Its structure was thought to be

```
                    R
                    |
                    C
                  //   \
               O         O
               |    H    |
       Cl      |    O    |      Cl
          \    |   / \   |    /
            Re · · · · · Re
          /    |   \ /   |  ↓  \
       Cl      |    O    |      Cl
               O    H    O
                 \       //
                    C
                    |
                    R
```

The oxidation state of the rhenium in this complex can either be regarded as rhenium (v) with a metal–metal bond or rhenium (IV) with spin pairing to account for the diamagnetism.

After removal of the purple crystals from n- or isobutyric acid reaction mixtures, the orange solutions deposited crystals of composition [ReO$_2$(O·CO·C$_3$H$_7$)]$_2$. Again the compounds were diamagnetic and non-conducting in nitrobenzene.[23] In addition to the usual carboxylate bands there was an additional very strong band at 935 cm^{-1} indicating the presence of an Re=O bond. These compounds are thought to contain both oxo- and carboxylate-bridging groups similar to those of the compounds [ReOCl(O·CO·R)]$_2$ but with a terminal oxygen group.

Rhenium pentachloride reacted with acetic acid to yield the compound ReCl$_3$(O·CO·CH$_3$)$_2$. This black crystalline complex was insoluble in all solvents and was diamagnetic. It was suggested that it contained seven-coordinate rhenium (v) but this would not explain its insolubility and it is likely that it is polymeric.

Freshly prepared hydrated rhenium dioxide dissolved in oxalic acid solution and a black crystalline compound of formula ReO·C$_2$O$_4$·3H$_2$O was isolated.[24] The three molecules of water could not be removed so the complex was formulated as $H[Re(OH)_3C_2O_4 \cdot H_2O]$ or $H_2[Re(OH)_4C_2O_4]$. These formulations were supported by titration with alkali which indicated that the acid behaves primarily as a mono-basic acid but gradually changes to the dibasic form. An equilibrium in solution was proposed:

$$H[Re(OH)_3C_2O_4 \cdot H_2O] \rightleftharpoons H_2[Re(OH)_4C_2O_4].$$

Under suitable conditions salts of either of the acids could be isolated pure. The conductivities of these agreed with those expected for (1 + 1) and (2 + 1) electrolytes respectively. These salts were diamagnetic in the solid state and no adequate explanation for this was suggested.

Similar complexes were prepared by refluxing potassium hexachloro-rhenate(IV) in water with gallic acid.[25] The complexes were extracted with alcohol and isolated as deep brown crystals which gave stable solutions in acid solutions. Analysis gave the formula $H_2[Re(H_2O)_2(C_6H_2O_2 \cdot OH \cdot COO_2] \cdot 6H_2O$ and after drying at 110° the dihydrate was obtained. Various diamagnetic salts of this acid were also prepared.

Catechol reacted with potassium hexachlororhenate(IV) in boiling water to give a dark brown solution from which black crystals were obtained. Analysis showed them to be $ReO \cdot C_6H_4O_2 \cdot 3H_2O$. The water could not be removed without decomposition and since potentiometric studies on the solution showed the compound to be a monobasic acid the formulation $H[Re(OH)_3(C_6H_4O_2) \cdot H_2O]$ was suggested.[26]

Complexes of Re^{IV} with various organic acids have been prepared in which it is thought an oxygen bridge exists between two rhenium atoms in a binuclear anion. With oxalic,[27] citric,[28] tartaric[28] and gallic acids, complexes were obtained with the formulae $K_4[Re(OH)_6L_2O]$ where L represents the organic ligand. These complexes were all diamagnetic in the solid state and also in solution. With salicylic acid however[29] a paramagnetic mononuclear species $K_2[Re(OH)_4sal]$ was obtained. The oxalato complex was prepared by refluxing rhenium dioxide with oxalic acid solution in the presence of potassium oxalate for 70 hours. After cooling the solution ethanol was added to the red-brown solution. The resulting precipitate was then recrystallized from acetic acid solution. The remaining complexes were all prepared by refluxing potassium hexachlororhenate(IV) with an aqueous solution of the appropriate organic acid. The salts were isolated and purified in the same way as the oxalate.

Druce[30] claimed that rhenium tris(ethoxide), $Re(OEt)_3$, was formed as a dark brown solid by the interaction of rhenium trichloride in ether and sodium ethoxide in alcohol. The compound was decomposed by water and dilute acids and alkalis but it was stable in dry air. In the absense of air it decomposed below 100° to give impure rhenium metal.

Sulphur Ligands

Few complexes of rhenium with sulphur ligands have been reported.

Dialkyldithiocarbamates of Re^{III} with the unusual stoichiometry $ReCl_2(NR_2CS_2)$ have been prepared by the interaction of rhenium trichloride and alkali metal salts of dimethyl-, diethyl-, and dibutyldithiocarbamates.[31] The compounds were obtained as stable brown crystals, readily soluble in acetone and alcohol, moderately soluble in chloroform and nitrobenzene and insoluble in water. The complexes were diamagnetic in the solid state and non-electrolytes in nitrobenzene solution.

Rhenium trichloride reacted with 3,4-dimethylthiotoluene to give a complex Re_2Cl_4L similar to those formed with 1,10-phenanthroline and 2,2'-dipyrridyl. In contrast 1,2-dimethylthiotoluene gave a red diamagnetic complex $ReCl_3L$ which was soluble in organic solvent and closely resembled the 5-coordinate complexes formed with 1,10-phenanthroline and 2,2'-dipyridyl.[5]

References

1. M. TSIN-SHEN and V. G. TRONEV, *Zh. Neorgan. Khim.* **5**, 861 (1960).
2. V. G. TRONEV and G. K. BABESHKINA, *Zh. Neorgan. Khim.* **3**, 2458 (1958).
3. G. K. BABESHKINA and V. G. TRONEV, *Zh. Neorgan. Khim.* **7**, 215 (1962).
4. R. COLTON and G. WILKINSON, *Chem. Ind. London* 1314 (1959).
5. R. COLTON, R. LEVITUS and G. WILKINSON, *J. Chem. Soc.* 4121 (1960).
6. V. G. TRONEV and S. M. BONDIN, *Dokl. Akad. Nauk SSSR* **86**, 87 (1952).
7. B. SUR and D. SEN, *Sci. Cult. Calcutta* **26**, 85 (1960).
8. A. S. KOTEL'NIKOVA and V. G. TRONEV, *Zh. Neorgan. Khim.* **3**, 1008 (1958).
9. V. V. LABEDINSKII and B. N. IVANOV-EMIN, *J. Gen. Chem. USSR* **13**, 253 (1943).
10. R. K. MURMAN and D. R. FOERSTER, *J. Phys. Chem.* **67**, 1383 (1963).
11. M. FRENI and V. VALENTI, *J. Inorg. Nucl. Chem.* **16**, 240 (1961).
12. C. J. L. LOCK and G. WILKINSON, *Chem. Ind. London* 40, (1962).
13. J. CHATT and G. A. ROWE, *Chem. Ind. London* 92 (1962).
14. J. CHATT and G. A. ROWE, *J. Chem. Soc.* 4019 (1962).
15. J. CHATT, J. D. GARFORTH, N. P. JOHNSON and G. A. ROWE, *J. Chem. Soc.* 601 (1964).
16. H. W. W. EHRLICH and P. G. OWSTON, *J. Chem. Soc.* 4368 (1963).
17. L. MALATESTA, M. FRENI and V. VALENTI, *Angew. Chem.* **73**, 273 (1961).
18. N. F. CURTIS, J. E. FERGUSSON and R. S. NYHOLM, *Chem. Ind. London* 625 (1958).
19. J. E. FERGUSSON and R. S. NYHOLM, *Chem. Ind. London* 1555 (1958).
20. A. EARNSHAW, B. N. FIGGIS, J. LEWIS and R. D. PEACOCK, *J. Chem. Soc.* 3132 (1961).
21. J. E. FERGUSSON and R. S. NYHOLM, *Nature* **183**, 1039 (1959).
22. J. E. FERGUSSON and R. S. NYHOLM, *Chem. Ind. London* 347 (1960).
23. F. TAHA and G. WILKINSON, *J. Chem. Soc.* 5406 (1963).
24. D. SEN and P. RAY, *J. Indian Chem. Soc.* **30**, 171 (1953).

25. D. SEN and P. RAY, *J. Indian Chem. Soc.* **30**, 181 (1953).
26. D. SEN and P. RAY, *J. Indian Chem. Soc.* **30**, 253 (1953).
27. B. JEZOWSKA-TRZEBIATOWSKA and S. WAJDA, *Bull. Acad. Polon. Sci., Ser. Sci. Chim.* **6**, 217 (1958).
28. B. J. JEZOWSKA-TRZEBIATOWSKA and S. WAJDA, *Bull. Acad. Polon. Sci., Ser. Sci. Chim.* **9**, 57 (1961).
29. B. JEZOWSKA-TRZEBIATOWSKA and W. WAJCIECHOWSKI, *Bull. Acad. Polon. Sci., Ser. Sci. Chim.* **9**, 65 (1961).
30. J. G. F. DRUCE, *J. Chem. Soc.* 1407 (1937).
31. R. COLTON, R. LEVITUS and G. WILKINSON, *J. Chem. Soc.* 5275 (1960).

7

Organometallic Compounds

The organometallic chemistry of technetium is as yet largely unexplored but that of rhenium has been the subject of intensive research. Rhenium carbonyl and the pentacarbonyl halides were discovered about 1940 but it has been only in the last few years, in the period of rapid development of transition-metal organic chemistry following the synthesis of the first cyclopentadienyl compounds, that many of the rhenium compounds have been prepared and studied.

Many of the rhenium compounds are stable and they are particularly interesting because in them rhenium shows its closest similarities to manganese.

Carbonyl Compounds

Rhenium carbonyl.—Rhenium carbonyl is most easily prepared by treating rhenium heptaoxide with carbon monoxide at 250° and 200 atmospheres pressure for 16 hours.[1] A more convenient starting material is potassium perrhenate, but in this case somewhat more vigorous conditions are required, 270° and 250 atmospheres pressure being recommended.[1] Rhenium heptasulphide has also been used as the starting material for the preparation of the carbonyl but it is interesting to note that the metal does not react. Yields are usually quantitative although in the preparation using rhenium heptaoxide pyrophoric rhenium metal is occasionally obtained, confirming that the metal is unreactive. The carbonyl may be purified by sublimation or recrystallization from organic solvents.

Rhenium carbonyl forms colourless, monoclinic crystals of typical carbonyl character and cryoscopic measurements have shown it to be dimeric. In a sealed tube it melts at 177°, but it decomposes above its melting point. Decomposition is complete at 400° giving only the metal

115

and carbon monoxide.[1] It is however quite stable at room temperature and is resistant to attack by dilute acids and alkalis and also concentrated hydrochloric acid, but it is attacked by hot oxidizing acids.

Although alkalis do not react with rhenium carbonyl to give the salt of the carbonyl hydride, the reaction between rhenium heptasulphide and carbon monoxide in the presence of a trace of water or hydrogen gave a volatile evil smelling rhenium compound. Although the compound was not characterized at that time, Hieber[1] suggested that it was the carbonyl hydride, $Re(CO)_5H$. It was found to be thermally decomposed to the carbonyl and hydrogen and in view of later research it appears very likely that this material was in fact the hydride.

Hieber[1] showed that rhenium carbonyl is dimeric and he proposed a structure involving carbon monoxide bridges

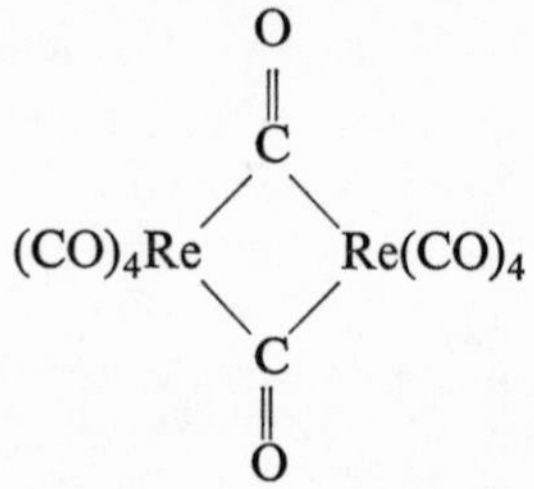

$$
\begin{array}{c}
O \\
\parallel \\
C \\
(CO)_4Re \diagup \quad \diagdown Re(CO)_4 \\
\diagdown \quad \diagup \\
C \\
\parallel \\
O
\end{array}
$$

On the basis of an infra-red study of the carbonyl this structure was shown to be incorrect.[2] There are three stretching frequencies, all very strong, and no absorption in the range usually associated with bridging carbonyl groups (1700–1900 cm^{-1}). The main frequencies are tabulated in Table 7-1.

Table 7-1. Infra-red absorption spectrum of rhenium carbonyl[2]

Phase	Carbonyl stretching modes (cm^{-1})			Metal–carbon
gas	2070	2019	1985	
CHCl$_3$ soln.	2067	2008	1965	
CS$_2$ soln.	2065	2006	1968	582, 574

The observed spectrum and diamagnetism of the compound were explained in terms of a *pseudo-ring* of six carbon monoxide groups situated between the two metal atoms and perpendicular to the metal–metal axis. This postulate was short-lived however when it was shown by x-ray diffraction studies that the dimeric molecule was held together by a metal–metal bond.[3]

Hieber and Fuchs[1] had found that rhenium carbonyl was monoclinic and they gave a ratio of $a:b:c = 1.04:1:2.045$ with $\beta = 76° 28'$. Dahl and coworkers[3] also found the compound to be monoclinic (space group Ia or $12/a$, four dimers per unit cell) with the lattice constants $a = 14.70$ Å; $b = 7.15$ Å and $c = 14.91$ Å with $\beta = 106°$; this gives a ratio $a:b:c = 2.05:1:2.08$. They showed that the dimer has approximately D_{4d} symmetry with direct metal–metal bonds and no bridging carbonyl groups. Each metal atom is octahedrally coordinated to five carbon monoxide groups and to the other metal atom in such a way that the joined octahedra are rotated 45° with respect to each other producing a staggered carbon monoxide configuration about the metal–metal axis. The metal–metal bond is very long (3.02 Å) compared to the covalent bond distance for rhenium (2.56 Å).

A partial vibrational analysis of the D_{4d} structure showed that three carbon monoxide stretching frequencies were to be expected in agreement with the observed spectrum. Only two metal–carbon stretching frequencies were observed instead of the three expected from D_{4d} symmetry but this was thought to be due to inadequate resolution in the 600 cm^{-1} region of the spectrum.

The polarographic reduction of rhenium carbonyl has been studied in absolute alcohol using 0.3 M tetramethylammonium chloride as the supporting electrolyte.[4] A two-electron reduction was observed corresponding to reduction to the pentacarbonyl anion $[Re(CO)_5]^-$.

Technetium carbonyl.—Technetium carbonyl has been prepared by the action of carbon monoxide (initially 200 atmospheres at 25°) at 220° on technetium heptaoxide for 20 hours.[5] The product was extracted with ether, the solution evaporated and the residue sublimed at 50° (10^{-2} mm). The colourless crystals, after recrystallization from pentane and two sublimations, had a melting point of 159–160°. There was some evidence of slow decomposition on exposure to the atmosphere. Technetium carbonyl decomposed on heating in a vacuum to carbon monoxide and the metal. The molecular weight showed the molecule to be a dimer and it was found to be diamagnetic. The infra-red spectrum in the carbonyl stretching region was found to be very similar to those of manganese and rhenium carbonyls and the absorptions are shown in Table 7-2.

Table 7-2. Carbonyl stretching frequencies of the group VII carbonyls (CCl$_4$ soln.)[5]

$Mn_2(CO)_{10}$	2044 m	2012 s	1981 m
$Tc_2(CO)_{10}$	2064 m	2016 s	1981 m
$Re_2(CO)_{10}$	2070 m	2012 s	1974 m

Very similar results to these have been obtained by Hieber and Herget.[6] Technetium carbonyl has been shown to be monoclinic and isomorphous with rhenium carbonyl.[7]

$$a = 14.73 \pm 0.05,\ b = 7.22 \pm 0.02,\ c = 14.90 \pm 0.02\ \text{Å}$$

$$\beta = 104.6° \pm 0.1°\ \text{Space group } Ia \text{ or } I2/a.$$

Technetium tetracarbonyl.—A second carbonyl of technetium, technetium tetracarbonyl, which has no known analogue with either manganese or rhenium, has recently been characterized.[8] It was formed as a side product in the preparation of technetium carbonyl hydride. By treatment of technetium pentacarbonyl, $Tc_2(CO)_{10}$, with sodium amalgam the intermediate $NaTc(CO)_5$ was obtained, but it was also noticed that some carbon monoxide was evolved and a reddish colour developed in the solution. After acidification with phosphoric acid, unreacted technetium pentacarbonyl and technetium pentacarbonyl hydride were removed by a series of solvent extraction and sublimation procedures. A final recrystallization from cyclohexane gave light tan platelets of technetium tetracarbonyl.

Technetium tetracarbonyl is stable in air although its solutions in cyclohexane appeared to decompose slowly. Addition of bromine to these solutions yielded technetium tetracarbonylbromide, identified by its infra-red spectrum. The tetracarbonyl was quantitatively converted to the pentacarbonyl by treatment with carbon monoxide at high temperature and pressure. A molecular weight determination of the compound in cyclohexane solution showed it to be trimeric.

Technetium tetracarbonyl shows four bands in the carbonyl stretching frequency region at 2093 (m); 2036 (s); 2014 (s) and 1989 (s) cm^{-1}. It is suggested[8] that the structure is similar to that of osmium tetracarbonyl consisting of a triangle of technetium atoms connected by metal–metal bonds. The similarity of this structure to that of caesium tetrachlororhenate(III) (see chapter 5) is obvious.

Rhenium carbonyl hydride.—Rhenium carbonyl hydride, $HRe(CO)_5$, has been isolated by treating the corresponding sodium salt with phosphoric acid.[9] The sodium salt $NaRe(CO)_5$ was prepared by reducing rhenium carbonyl with 1% sodium amalgam in tetrahydrofuran solution. The hydride is a colourless air-sensitive liquid. It is weakly acidic, insoluble in water and melts at 12.5°. It is more stable than the corresponding carbonyl hydrides of iron and cobalt but it is quantitatively decomposed to the parent carbonyl and hydrogen at 100°C.

The infra-red spectra of the hydride and the corresponding deuteride, prepared by treating the sodium salt with deuterophosphoric acid, have been studied.[10] Bands at 1832 and 1318 cm^{-1} were assigned to the Re–H and Re–D stretches respectively. The spectra were generally similar to those of the corresponding manganese compounds and suggested low symmetry in the molecule. The spectra in the carbonyl stretching frequency range were complicated but the main bands were at 2031 and 2021 cm $^{-1}$ for the hydride and the deuteride respectively.

The vapour pressure of rhenium carbonyl hydride, measured between 6–100°, is given by the equation $\log p = 8.598 - (2353.6/T)$ and the heat of evaporation was calculated as 10.76 kcal/mole.[10]

Technetium carbonyl hydride.—Technetium carbonyl was reduced by sodium amalgam in tetrahydrofuran solution. At this stage the infra-red spectrum of the solution in the carbonyl region was very similar to the spectra of the manganese and rhenium pentacarbonyl anions (Table 7-3).[11] Acidification with phosphoric acid gave a complex reaction. Hydrogen was evolved and bands due to technetium carbonyl appeared in the infra-red spectrum. Technetium tetracarbonyl has also been isolated from the reaction products, but despite these side reactions some technetium carbonyl hydride was isolated from the mixture. After distillation its infra-red spectrum was found to be very similar to those of manganese and rhenium carbonyl hydrides as shown in Table 7-3.

Table 7-3. Infra-red spectra of some pentacarbonyl compounds[11]

$M(CO)_5{}^-$	Mn	1898 s	1864 s
	Tc	1911 s	1865 s
	Re	1910 s	1864 s
$HM(CO)_5$	Mn	2014 s	2007 m
	Tc	2021 s	2015 m
	Re	2015 s	2006 m

Carbonyl Halides

Two distinct series of rhenium carbonyl halides are known, the simple monomeric pentacarbonyl halides, $Re(CO)_5X$[12, 13] and the binuclear tetracarbonyl halides $[Re(CO)_4X]_2$ (X = Cl, Br, I).[14]

Rhenium pentacarbonyl halides.—The most readily prepared compound of these series is rhenium pentacarbonyl iodide which is formed by passing carbon monoxide at one atmosphere pressure over a ground mixture of potassium hexaiodorhenate (IV), K_2ReI_6, and copper powder at 200°.[13] In the absence of copper which combines with the liberated iodine the reaction proceeds according to the equation

$$K_2ReI_6 + 5\,CO \rightarrow Re(CO)_5I + 2\,KI + \frac{3}{2}\,I_2$$

I

and the product must be separated from the elementary iodine by sublimation. Quantitative yields are obtained at 125° using a pressure of 50 atmospheres of carbon monoxide.[13] In these early preparations the pentacarbonyl iodide was described as yellow, but later Brimm and coworkers[15] described it as white. It is now known that the pentacarbonyl iodide is in fact white and the dimeric tetracarbonyl iodide is deep yellow, and it seems certain that the original preparations contained some rhenium tetracarbonyl iodide as impurity.

Rhenium pentacarbonyl bromide[13] is formed on the surface of potassium hexabromorhenate (IV) if carbon monoxide is passed over the heated material, but quantitative yields are obtained only by using carbon monoxide pressures of 10 atmospheres at 200–300°. Rhenium pentacarbonyl bromide forms colourless needles.

Rhenium pentacarbonyl chloride, $Re(CO)_5Cl$, can also be prepared by this same general method, but other techniques have also been described.[13] It can, for example, be prepared from rhenium metal and cupric chloride under 210 atmospheres of carbon monoxide at 250°

$$Re + CuCl_2 + 6\ CO \rightarrow Re(CO)_5Cl + CuClCO$$

The yield is about 70% in the presence of excess cupric chloride, whereas with the bromide the yield is about 90%.

Potassium perrhenate reacts with carbon tetrachloride at 230° under a pressure of 200 atmospheres of carbon monoxide to give the pentacarbonyl chloride whilst the iodide can be prepared from potassium perrhenate with organic iodides, such as ethyl iodide and iodoform, at 200° and 200 atmospheres pressure of carbon monoxide.[13]

The rhenium pentacarbonyl halides are stable compounds, they can be sublimed in a vacuum or in a carbon dioxide atmosphere, the iodide subliming at 90° and the chloride at 140°. Rhenium pentacarbonyl iodide is converted to the chloride or bromide by passing a mixture of carbon monoxide and chlorine or bromine over it. Chlorine and bromine also displace the iodine in the iodide on gentle heating in benzene solution. The halogen cannot be removed from the rhenium pentacarbonyl halides to give the carbonyl by silver or by sodium in refluxing benzene.[1]

Rhenium pentacarbonyl iodide is soluble in petroleum ether at room temperature, but the chloride dissolves only in boiling benzene (see below). All of the compounds are insoluble in water, they are oxidized to perrhenate ion by a hot mixture of hydrogen peroxide and sodium hydroxide solution and by concentrated nitric acid.

The u.v. absorption spectra of the rhenium pentacarbonyl halides have been studied by Schuh.[16] All the measurements were done in dioxan for a medium of high dipole, or in hexane for a medium with no dipole. All of the compounds were soluble to the extent of about 0.1 M and could be recovered unchanged. In all cases absorption began at about 3600 Å, rose rapidly to a maximum at 3325 Å and then decreased to a minimum at 3015–3005 Å. After this the absorption increased again then remained constant in the range 2850–2550 Å before rising continuously into the ultra-violet. Rhenium pentacarbonyl iodide gave a slightly different spectrum which may be attributed to contamination by the tetracarbonyl iodide (see below).

The pentacarbonyl halides are polarographically reduced in absolute alcohol, tetramethylammonium iodide being used as the supporting electrolyte.[4] In all cases a two-electron reduction was observed corresponding to reduction to the pentacarbonyl anion $[Re(CO)_5]^-$. It was found, in accordance with chemical evidence, that the halides reduced more readily than the carbonyls themselves and that in the halide series the half-wave potentials were in the order $I < Br < Cl$.

Rhenium tetracarbonyl halides.—Rhenium tetracarbonyl halides of the type $[Re(CO)_4X]_2$ have been prepared by the thermal decomposition of the pentacarbonyl halides in inert high-boiling solvents above 100°.[14]

$$2 Re(CO)_5X \rightleftharpoons [Re(CO)_4X]_2 + 2 CO \quad (X = Cl, Br, I)$$

The compounds were shown to be dimeric by ebullioscopic determination of molecular weight in benzene. The tetracarbonyl halides are only sparingly soluble in most organic solvents but they can be recrystallized from chloroform or cyclohexane.

The tetracarbonyl halides decompose on heating without melting. The chloride and bromide form fine white needles, but the iodide gives yellow needles which probably accounts for the yellow hue reported previously by Hieber for the pentacarbonyl iodide. The tetracarbonyl halides may also be prepared by irradiating the pentacarbonyl derivatives in hexane with ultra-violet light.[14]

Nitric oxide does not react with the tetracarbonyl halides, but carbon monoxide reforms the pentacarbonyl halides under conditions of high temperature and pressure. Thus the equation representing their formation is reversible according to the conditions.

The most reasonable structure for the tetracarbonyl halides, in which there is a conventional halogen bridge, is

The infra-red spectra of the compounds as tabulated in Table 7-4 are consistent with this formulation.

In a more recent study[11] Hileman and coworkers have recorded two extra weak peaks for the pentacarbonyl halides and one additional weak peak for the tetracarbonyl halides. These are also given in Table 7-4 together with the data for the corresponding technetium compounds described in the next section.

Table 7-4. Carbonyl stretching frequencies of rhenium and technetium carbonyl halides

Compound	Solvent		C–O stretching modes			Ref.
$Re(CO)_5Cl$	CCl_4		2056		1987	14
$Re(CO)_5Cl$	CCl_4	2156 w	2045 s	2016 w	1982 m	11
$Re(CO)_5Br$	CCl_4		2057		1993	14
$Re(CO)_5Br$	CCl_4	2150 w	2045 s	2016 w	1984 m	11
$Re(CO)_5I$	CCl_4		2055		1995	14
$Re(CO)_5I$	CCl_4	2145 w	2042 s	2013 w	1987 m	11
$Tc(CO)_5Cl$	CCl_4	2153 w	2057 s	2028 w	1991 m	11
$Tc(CO)_5Br$	CCl_4	2150 w	2056 s	2027 w	1995 m	11
$Tc(CO)_5I$	CCl_4	2146 w	2055 s	2024 w	2000 m	11
$[Re(CO)_4Cl]_2$	$CHCl_3$		2043	2010	1964	14
$[Re(CO)_4Cl]_2$	CCl_4	2114 w	2032 s	2000 m	1959 m	11
$[Re(CO)_4Br]_2$	$CHCl_3$		2044	2012	1970	14
$[Re(CO)_4Br]_2$	CCl_4	2113 w	2031 s	2000 m	1964 m	11
$[Re(CO)_4I]_2$	$CHCl_3$		2042	2012	1971	14
$[Re(CO)_4I]_2$	CCl_4	2106 w	2029 s	2001 m	1965 m	11
$[Tc(CO)_4Cl]_2$	CCl_4	2119 w	2048 s	2011 m	1972 m	11
$[Tc(CO)_4Br]_2$	CCl_4	2116 w	2046 s	2012 m	1973 m	11
$[Tc(CO)_4I]_2$	CCl_4	2108 w	2042 s	2012 m	1975 m	11

Technetium carbonyl halides.—The first carbonyl halides of technetium to be prepared were the carbonyl iodides.[5] Technetium carbonyl reacted only slowly with iodine at 100°. In an evacuated tube or under a pressure of one atmosphere of carbon monoxide the product was technetium tetra-carbonyl iodide. However, under 50 atmospheres pressure of carbon monoxide the pentacarbonyl iodide was obtained. Subsequently[11] the chlorides and bromides were also reported. Technetium carbonyl was dissolved in carbon tetrachloride saturated with chlorine at 25°. Colourless crystals separated after about an hour, the infra-red spectrum showed the crystals to be a mixture of both the pentacarbonyl chloride and the tetra-carbonyl chloride. The mixed chlorides were treated with carbon monoxide at 80 atmospheres pressure at 100° for 40 hours and pure technetium pentacarbonyl chloride was obtained. Heating this in air at 100° gave the tetracarbonyl chloride.

Similar reactions between technetium carbonyl and bromine gave practically pure pentacarbonyl bromide which was converted to the tetracarbonyl bromide by heating at 100°. The infra-red spectra of these compounds are given in Table 7-4.

Substitution Products of Rhenium Carbonyl and Carbonyl Halides

Rhenium carbonyl has been said to react with pyridine to give bis(pyridine) rhenium tricarbonyl, $py_2Re(CO)_3$. Similarly o-phenanthroline gave a compound $(o\text{-phen})Re(CO)_3$.[17] The pyridine compound was pale yellow and the o-phenanthroline compound deep yellow. They were very stable compounds, unaffected by dilute or concentrated hydrochloric acid although they were decomposed by oxidizing acids.

Wilkinson[18] was unable to repeat the preparation of these compounds. The red solutions reported by Hieber[17] were obtained but the yellow crystals of the substitution products proved to be elusive.

Rhenium pentacarbonyl chloride also reacted with refluxing pyridine with evolution of carbon monoxide to form bis(pyridine) rhenium tricarbonyl chloride, $py_2Re(CO)_3Cl$. According to Hieber[17] the pentacarbonyl bromide and iodide were more resistant to attack and had to be heated with pyridine in a sealed tube at 240° for eight hours to produce analogous compounds. As with the carbonyl, o-phenanthroline reacted rather more readily to give compounds such as $(o\text{-phen})Re(CO)_3Cl$, the colour and stability being similar to those of the compounds derived from the carbonyl.

Aniline reacted with rhenium pentacarbonyl chloride at 120° to give the colourless compound bis(aniline) rhenium tricarbonyl chloride $[(C_6H_5NH_2)_2Re(CO)_3Cl]$ which was readily converted to the corresponding o-phenanthroline complex by heating with o-phenanthroline in ethanol at 65°.

Similar reactions were observed with p-tolylisonitrile and triphenylphosphine but in these cases the products were formulated as tetracarbonyl derivatives $[Re(CO)_4(CH_3 \cdot C_6H_4NC)_2]Cl$ and $[Re(CO)_4[P(C_6H_5)_3]_2]Cl$.[17] It has been shown conclusively that the triphenylphosphine derivative has been wrongly formulated and that it is a tricarbonyl derivative entirely analogous to the pyridine, o-phenanthroline and aniline compounds. No doubt the same is also true of the p-tolylisonitrile compound, particularly as Hieber observed that both of these compounds treated readily with pyridine to give bis(pyridine) rhenium tricarbonyl chloride.

Wilkinson and coworkers found that these same substitution products could be prepared from the tetracarbonyl halides.[14, 19] Pyridine reacted with rhenium tetracarbonyl iodide, splitting the halogen bridge to give (py)$_2$Re(CO)$_3$I. Further substitution products with triphenylphosphine and triphenylarsine were made by direct action of the ligand on either the pentacarbonyl halide (method A, cf. Hieber[17]) or the tetracarbonyl halide (method B).

Method A. Re(CO)$_5$X + 2 L → L$_2$Re(CO)$_3$X + 2 CO

Method B. [Re(CO)$_4$X]$_2$ + 4 L → 2 L$_2$Re(CO)$_3$X + 2 CO (X = Cl, Br, I)

In every case reaction was faster with the tetracarbonyl halide. The infra-red spectra of some of these substitution products in the carbonyl stretching region are shown in Table 7-5.

Table 7-5. Infra-red spectra of substituted rhenium carbonyl halides

Compound	Prep.	Carbonyl stretching modes (cm^{-1})		
py$_2$Re(CO)$_3$Cl	A	2041	1934	1891
py$_2$Re(CO)$_3$I	B	2041	1934	1891
(dipy)Re(CO)$_3$I	A	2037	1932	1903
(PPh$_3$)$_2$Re(CO)$_3$Cl	A + B	2050	1961	1901
(PPh$_3$)$_2$Re(CO)$_3$I	A	2049	1966	1904
(AsPh$_3$)$_2$Re(CO)$_3$Cl	B	2049	1960	1904
(AsPh$_3$)$_2$Re(CO)$_3$I	A + B	2047	1961	1908

It is clear from the table that the triphenylphosphine compound is a member of the series of tricarbonyl derivatives and the fact that it was prepared[19] from the tetracarbonyl halides with evolution of carbon monoxide confirms that the original formulation was incorrect.

The configuration of bis(pyridine) rhenium tricarbonyl iodide has been reasonably deduced by considering the nature of the ligands present and their ability to produce the *trans* effect.[20, 21]

I   II   III

Arguing from the pentacarbony odide (I) the carbon monoxide group predicted to be most labile would be those *cis* to the iodine atom since iodine has a lower *trans* effect than carbon monoxide. The first substitution product (II) was assumed as an intermediate although it was never isolated. In structure II the active carbonyls would be those *cis* to both iodine and pyridine since both of these groups have smaller *trans* effects than carbon monoxide,[21] which leads to structure III for the disubstituted compound. Commencing with the tetracarbonyl iodine, similar arguments based on the comparative *trans* effect of the various groups showed that the same disubstitution product should be obtained. That this is so is clear by reference to Table 7-6. Similar arguments may be used for the other substituted compounds and the fact that *o*-phenanthroline and dipyridyl complexes can be prepared with spectra identical to those of the other complexes confirms that the monodentate ligands substitute in *cis* positions.

The triphenylphosphine derivative of the carbonyl chlorides described above has also been prepared by the action of carbon monoxide on bis-(triphenylphosphine) rhenium dichloride.[22] In addition bis(triphenylphosphine) rhenium dicarbonyl chloride was also formed. Bis(triphenylphosphine) rhenium dibromide gave similar compounds but the corresponding iodide gave only bis(triphenylphosphine) rhenium carbonyl iodide. The compounds and some of their properties are given in Table 7-6.

Table 7-6. Bis(triphenylphosphine)rhenium carbonyl halides

Compound	Colour	Solubility	Conductivity in nitrobenzene 2×10^{-3} M
$(PPh_3)_2Re(CO)_2Cl$	ivory	v. sol. $CHCl_3$; CH_2Cl_2	0.1
$(PPh_3)_2Re(CO)_3Cl$	yellow	sl. sol. C_6H_6; $C_6H_5 \cdot NO_2$	0.1
$(PPh_3)_2Re(CO)_2Br$	orange-yellow	insol. C_2H_5OH; $(C_2H_5)_2O$	0.1
$(PPh_3)_2Re(CO)_3Br$	orange	v. sol. $CHCl_3$; CH_2Cl_2	0.1
$(PPh_3)_2Re(CO)I$	blue	C_6H_6; $C_6H_5NO_2$ insol. in other solvents	0.05

Rhenium pentacarbonyl chloride reacts with liquid ammonia.[23] After evaporating off the excess liquid ammonia a colourless crystalline mass was obtained which was extracted with acetone to give two products. The compound soluble in acetone was found to be $[Re(CO)_4NH_3 \cdot Cl]$. The residue, insoluble in acetone, was recrystallized from methanol and found to be $[Re(CO)_4(NH_3)_2]Cl$. In contrast to the case of the triphenylphosphine derivative, the formulation of this compound as a tetracarbonyl is probably correct since it can be quantitatively precipitated with sodium tetraphenyl boron to give $[Re(CO)_4(NH_3)_2][B(C_6H_5)_4]$. Nevertheless when heated with pyridine at 120° the tetracarbonyl diammine gave bis(pyridine)

rhenium tricarbonyl chloride and the tetracarbonyl monoammine with
o-phenanthroline in ethanol gave *o*-phenanthroline rhenium tricarbonyl
chloride.

These substitution reactions of rhenium pentacarbonyl chloride are
summarized in the following scheme.

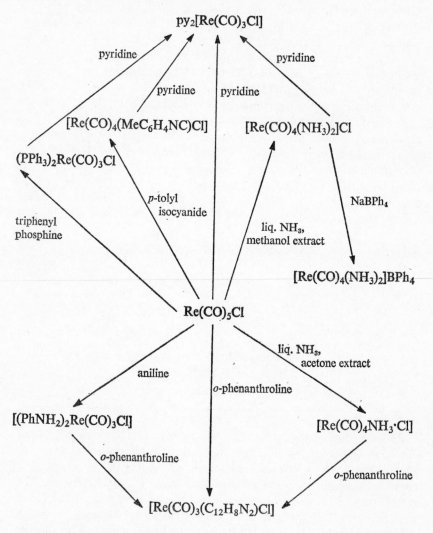

Hieber and Schuster[24] reported that rhenium pentacarbonyl chloride
reacted with potassium cyanide to give a carbonylcyanide anion $[Re(CO)_4$
$(CN)_2]^-$. They also reported that rhenium carbonyl and the pentacarbanyl

halides reacted with 2 M potassium hydroxide in methanol solution, the carbonyl slowly at 100° and the halides readily at 50–60°. The reaction schemes suggested were

$$Re_2(CO)_{10} + 3\,KOH \xrightarrow{H_2O} K[Re_2(CO)_8O_2H] + K_2CO_3 + 2\,H_2 + CO$$

$$2\,Re(CO)_5Cl + 3\,KOH \longrightarrow K[Re_2(CO)_8O_2H] + 2\,KCl + 2\,CO + H_2O$$

The carbonyl salt was soluble in acetone, methanol and ethanol, its conductivity in acetone corresponded to that of a binary electrolyte. The diamagnetic anion was formulated as having oxo- and hydroxo-bridges

$$[(CO)_4Re \underset{\diagdown OH\diagup}{\overset{\diagup O\diagdown}{}} Re(CO)_4]^-$$

This rather unlikely structure requires more confirmation, Hieber and Schuster[24] also showed that thiophenol reacted with rhenium pentacarbonyl chloride in benzene solution to give a compound $[(CO)_4RePhS]_2$ which was diamagnetic and stable.

$$2\,Re(CO)_5Cl + 2\,PhSH \rightarrow [(CO)_4RePhS]_2 + 2\,HCl + 2\,CO$$

It was formulated as having sulphur bridges

$$\begin{array}{c} C_6H_5 \\ | \\ S \\ \diagup \diagdown \\ (CO)_4Re \qquad Re(CO)_4 \\ \diagdown \diagup \\ S \\ | \\ C_6H_5 \end{array}$$

A hexacarbonyl cation of Re^I has been prepared by the action of carbon monoxide on rhenium pentacarbonyl chloride at high temperature and pressure in the presence of aluminium chloride.[25]

$$Re(CO)_5Cl + AlCl_3 + CO \rightarrow [Re(CO)_6]AlCl_4$$

The cation gives very stable diamagnetic salts with large anions such as perchlorate and tetraphenylborate. This very unusual cation shows only one band in the carbonyl region at 2083 cm^{-1}.[26]

Organorhenium Pentacarbonyls

A series of acyl rhenium pentacarbonyls[27] and perfluoroacyl pentacarbonyls[28] of the general formula $RCORe(CO)_5$ have been prepared where $RCO = CH_3CO$, C_6H_5CO, C_2F_5CO etc. In all cases the preparative technique used has been to reduce rhenium carbonyl in tetrahydrofuran with sodium amalgam to give a pale yellow air sensitive solution of $NaRe(CO)_5$ and then to treat this with the appropriate halide $RCOCl$. The compounds were all very volatile and they had the unusual property that on heating above their melting points the acyl group lost its molecule of carbon monoxide to give the corresponding alkyl derivative,

for example $CH_3CORe(CO)_5 \rightarrow CH_3Re(CO)_5 + CO$

The compounds obtained are listed in Table 7-7.

Table 7-7. Organorhenium pentacarbonyls

Compound	M.p.	Dipole (D.)	Ref.
$CH_3CORe(CO)_5$	80–81	2.47 ± 0.06	27
$CH_3Re(CO)_5$*	120		27
$C_6H_5CORe(CO)_5$	about 120 (decomp.)	2.54 ± 0.07	27
$C_6H_5Re(CO)_5$	46–47	1.18 ± 0.10	27
$C_6H_5 \cdot CH_2Re(CO)_5$**	33–34		27
$C_2F_5CORe(CO)_5$	81–83		28
$C_2F_5Re(CO)_5$	39–40		28
$C_3F_7CORe(CO)_5$	54		28
$C_3F_7Re(CO)_5$	27		28

*   Also prepared by interaction of CH_3I and $NaRe(CO)_5$[9].
** Prepared by interaction of $C_6H_5 \cdot CH_2Cl$ and $NaRe(CO)_5$.

The infra-red spectra of some of these compounds have been observed, they are complex in the carbonyl stretching region.[29] The principle absorptions are shown in Table 7-8.

Table 7-8. Carbonyl stretching frequencies in some organorhenium pentacarbonyls

Compound	$\nu_{=C=O}$					$\nu_{>C=O}$
$CH_3CORe(CO)_5$	2131 w-m	2068 m	2061 m	2045 m	2018 ss	1617
		2001 m-s	1976 w-m			
$CH_3Re(CO)_5$	2125 w-m	2068 w	2040 w-m	2010 ss	1979 m-s	
$C_6H_5CORe(CO)_5$	2134 m	2068 m	2018 ss	2001 s	1978 m	1568
$C_6H_5Re(CO)_5$	2132 m	2070 m	2021 ss	1991 s		
$C_6H_5 \cdot CH_2 \cdot Re(CO)_5$	2126 m	2070 m	2053 w	2015 ss	1986 s	

Cyclopentadienyl Compounds

Bis-π-cyclopentadienyl rhenium hydride.—One of the general ways of preparing transition metal cyclopentadienyl compounds is to react the metal halide with sodium cyclopentadienide. Rhenium pentachloride was added to a solution of sodium cyclopentadienide in tetrahydrofuran solution; after reaction was complete the solvent was removed under vacuum to give a purplish solid. Vacuum sublimation produced a lemon yellow solid (m.p. 161–162°) in about 20% yield.[30] Its molecular weight in benzene was shown to be 312 ± 5 and at first the compound was thought to be bis-π-cyclopentadienyl rhenium, but this supposition was shown to be incorrect when it was found that the compound was diamagnetic.

A typical n.m.r. spectrum of a saturated solution of the compound in benzene or carbon disulphide showed two peaks, the first at 45 ± 2 c/s (at 40 Mc/s) and the second at 733 ± 2 c/s.[30, 31] The relative areas of the peaks was 10:1 respectively. The first resonance lay in the region where the protons of ferrocene and other π-cyclopentadienyl compounds absorb[32] and was obviously attributable to the protons in the two equivalent cyclopentadiene rings. The small peak at high fields could only be attributed to a proton which was very well shielded and led to the postulate that the compound was bis-π-cyclopentadienyl rhenium hydride $(C_5H_5)_2ReH$. This was one of the first examples recorded of the very large shifts for hydridic protons. Similar effects have since been observed for many hydrides including cobalt carbonyl hydride, $HCo(CO)_4$,[33] iron carbonyl hydride, $H_2Fe(CO)_4$,[34] and platinum phosphine hydrides of the type $HPt(PPh)_3)_3$.[35] The phenomenon has now become a diagnostic test for the presence of a transition-metal hydride.

The infra-red spectra of bis-π-cyclopentadienyl rhenium hydride and the corresponding deuteride $(C_5H_5)_2ReD$ have been measured over the range 625–3400 cm^{-1} in carbon disulphide solution, in mulls and with single crystals.[31] Whilst the spectra were generally similar to that of ferrocene, a band at about 2000 cm^{-1} of comparable intensity to that due to the C–H stretch appeared in the solution spectrum of the hydride. In the single crystal and mull spectra of the hydride there was a split in this new peak, presumably due to crystal effects. The deuteride showed similar peaks but they were displaced to about 1460 cm^{-1}. Hence, the assignment of the sharp band at 2000 cm^{-1} in the hydride to the rhenium–hydrogen stretching mode was certain. For the solid state spectra $\nu_{Re-H}/\nu_{Re^-D} = 1.396$ and 1.397 for the two peaks respectively, these high values suggest a very strong metal–hydrogen bond which is consistent with the considerable thermal stability of the compound. The infra-red data is summarized in Table 7-9.

Table 7-9. Infra-red spectra of $(C_5H_5)_2ReH$ and $(C_5H_5)_2ReD$

Compound	State	C–H	Re–H	Re–D
$(C_5H_5)_2ReH$	CS$_2$ sol.	3100 (w)	2030 (w)	
$(C_5H_5)_2ReH$	crystal	3070 (w)	2037 (w) 2000 (w)	
$(C_5H_5)_2ReD$	crystal	3100 (w)		1458 (w) 1432 (w)

Examination of the mass spectrum[36] of bis-π-cyclopentadienyl rhenium hydride unequivocally showed the presence of the ion $C_{10}H_{11}Re^+$. The data are shown in Table 7-10 and indicate that the π-bonded rings are probably more stable than in ferrocene and cobaltacene.

Table 7-10. Mass spectrum of $(C_5H_5)_2ReH$

Ion	Relative yield of ions
$C_{10}H_{11}Re^+$	100
$C_{10}H_{10}Re^+$	71.5
$C_{10}H_9Re^+$	—
$C_8H_8Re^+$	3.7
$C_8H_7Re^+$	35.6
$C_8H_6Re^+$	9.30
$C_6H_4Re^+$	9.0
Re^+	3.5

Incidental to this study, the isotopic ratio of $^{185}Re/^{187}Re$ was determined as 0.59, a value in good agreement with the value obtained by White and Cameron.[37]

Bis-π-cyclopentadienyl rhenium hydride forms lemon yellow crystals, which after recrystallization from benzene, ether or high boiling petroleum ether melt at 161–162°. It is thermally stable to at least 250° and it sublimes readily above 80° in a vacuum. In carbon tetrachloride the hydride decomposed rapidly to give chloroform and an insoluble material, which contained no biscyclopentadienyl cations.[31] The formulation of chloroform from carbon tetrachloride is a fairly general reaction for transition metal hydrides.[38]

The solid is unaffected by water and it reacts only slowly with atmospheric oxygen although its solutions are rapidly decomposed by air. It is sparingly soluble in liquid ammonia in which it is a non-electrolyte. It does not form ammoniates as do bis-π-cyclopentadienyl vanadium and chromium,[39] and it does not react with ferrous chloride in tetrahydrofuran to give ferrocene.[31]

Bis-π-cyclopentadienyl rhenium hydride does not react with nitric oxide or diazomethane at ordinary pressures, but carbon monoxide does react with it at 100° and 200 atmospheres pressure to give a compound with the formula $C_{10}H_{11}Re(CO)_2$[40] which will be discussed in a later section.

The hydride is not affected by 8 N sodium hydroxide, but it does dissolve in dilute hydrochloric and sulphuric acids without effervescence. The resulting colourless solutions gave the usual tests chacteristic of a large cyclopentadienyl cation, for instance it gave a reineckate precipitate which was characterized.[31] The reaction has been shown to be

$$(C_5H_5)_2ReH + HCl \rightarrow [(C_5H_5)_2ReH_2]^+Cl^-$$

Addition of ammonia or sodium hydroxide to these solutions liberated the free base, that is the hydride, which could be recovered quantitatively by solvent extraction. The solid hydride readily absorbed gaseous hydrogen chloride or hydrogen bromide, forming the salts quantitatively as amorphous, extremely hygroscopic white powders. Excess of hydrogen chloride gave a strong pink colour which disappeared as the excess hydrogen chloride was pumped off. It has been suggested that the colour may be due to an easily dissociated species $[(C_5H_5)_2ReH_2]^+HCl_2^-$ similar to the salts formed by caesium and other large cations.[41, 42, 43] The system $(C_5H_5)_2ReH-$ $[(C_5H_5)_2ReH_2]Cl$ is analogous to the NH_3-NH_4OH system except that the base is insoluble in water. Determination of the base constant[31] by pH measurement and titrations of $(C_5H_5)_2ReH$ at 25° with acid, and of $[(C_5H_5)_2ReH_2]Cl$ with base in 60% dioxan solution gave a pK value of 8.5. The value for ammonia in 60% dioxan interpolated from published data is 8.85.[44]

There are several possible structures for bis-π-cyclopentadienyl rhenium hydride and the protonated cation derived from it and these have been discussed in some detail.[31] Liehr has suggested that the single hydrogen atom in the hydride and the two hydrogen atoms in the cation can be located between the cyclopentadienyl rings and the metal.[45] The hydrogen atoms were considered to be in the $d(a, g)$ orbital which, according to the molecular orbital view of the bonding in neutral bis-π-cyclopentadienyl metal complexes, is non-bonding as far as the primary metal ring bonding is concerned.

Of other possible structures there are two major types, those with the rings parallel to each other as in ferrocene (type A) or at an angle to each other as in bis-π-cyclopentadienyl tin[46] (type B).

Type A   Type B

Recent theoretical studies have indicated that in type B structures three molecular orbitals are available to accommodate protons (as in bis-π-cyclopentadienyl tantalum trihydride) and that the stability of the ring systems is not seriously reduced even when the angle between the rings is reduced to 150 degrees. Either of the main structural types could equally well account for the large chemical shift of the hydric proton in the n.m.r. spectrum and also for the basic character of the hydride.

The infra-red spectrum of the cation $[(C_5H_5)_2ReH_2]^+$ might have been expected to provide useful information, since, if the hydrogen atoms were symmetrically on either side of the metal (type A) only one metal–hydrogen stretch would be expected. For structures with the hydrogen at an angle (type B) both symmetric and asymmetric vibrations should be observed. Unfortunately, the rhenium–hydrogen stretching bonds are so weak that even by using concentrated aqueous solutions of the salt it was impossible to identify the bands reliably.[31] In the solid state spectrum of the hydride itself the peak is split although the solution spectrum shows only one band (Table 7-9). This phenomenon is difficult to reconcile with a type A structure since with the hydrogen atoms buried between the metal atom and the rings it is not easy to see how intermolecular interaction in the crystal lattice could affect such hydrogen atoms.

The n.m.r. data for the hydride and the protonated cation and the corresponding deuterides is shown in Table 7-11. All four compounds

Table 7-11. N.m.r. data (at 40 Mc/s) of the cyclopentadienyl rhenium hydrides and deuterides. (The high field side is designated—; shifts referred to water at $21 \pm 1°$)

Compound	Proton res.	Relative intensity	Assign.	Fine structure	Multiplet width	Splitting
$(C_5H_5)_2ReH$	− 46	10	π-C_5H_5	Doublet	1.9	1.05
in C_6H_6 or CS_2	− 732	1	hydridic	not detected	18	
$(C_5H_5)_2ReD$	− 46	—	π-C_5H_5	Singlet	0.5	
in C_6H_6	no hydride	—	—	—		
$[(C_5H_5)_2ReH_2]Cl$	+ 33	10	π-C_5H_5	Triplet	1.45	0.56
in water	− 734.5	2	hydridic	not detected	8	
$[(C_5H_5)_2ReD_2]Cl$	+ 32.5	—	π-C_5H_5	Singlet	0.5	
in water	no hydride	—	—	—		

showed the resonance due to the π-cyclopentadienyl rings, and the hydrides showed the shielded proton resonances. It has been argued that the fine structure of these peaks is more consistent with either a type A o type B structure than with Liehr's model with the proton(s) between the metal atom and the rings.[31] If the consequences of a type A or B structure are first considered, the absence of fine structure on the cyclopentadienyl peaks in the deuterides, and its appearance in the hydrides, suggests that this fine structure is produced by electron-coupled spin–spin interaction[47] between the hydridic proton(s) and the ring protons rather than being attributable to chemical shifts of non-equivalent cyclopentadienyl rings.

The single proton in the bis-π-cyclopentadienyl rhenium hydride should split the cyclopentadienyl peak into a symmetrical doublet, and the two equivalent protons in the cation should split the cyclopentadienyl peak into a triplet with intensity ratios $1:2:1$. The replacement of hydrogen by deuterium, which has a spin of 1, would be expected to split the cyclopentadienyl peak into a triplet in bis-π-cyclopentadienyl rhenium deuteride and a quintuplet in the deuterated cation, but the smaller magnetic moment of the deuteron would lead to smaller splittings. In fact a singlet was observed in both deutero compounds, any fine structure being completely obscured.

On Liehr's model of the hydride the cyclopentadienyl rings would not be equivalent as the hydrogen atom is located between one of them and the metal. Thus a double cyclopentadienyl peak would be expected in both the hydride and the deuteride and furthermore in the hydride these two peaks would be further split by unequal amounts by the hydridic proton. For the cations, the deuteride should give one peak, but in the normal cation the cyclopentadienyl peaks would be split into a doublet by the nearest proton and each further split into a doublet by the more distant proton.

It is clear that the experimental data supports a structure of type A or B rather than Liehr's model, but the n.m.r. data do not distinguish between these two structural types, and the final arbiter will almost certainly have to be x-ray diffraction.

Bis-π-cyclopentadienyl technetium.—A cyclopentadienyl derivative of technetium has been prepared by the action of sodium cyclopentadienide on technetium tetrachloride in tetrahydrofuran solution.[48] After stirring the reaction mixture for 4 hours at 50° in the absence of oxygen, sodium borohydride was added and the mixture again heated. After removal of the solvent a golden yellow air-sensitive compound was sublimed from the purple reaction mixture at 55–60° (0.1 mm).

The infra-red spectrum of the compound was similar to that of bis-π-cyclopentadienyl rhenium hydride except that no metal–hydrogen stretch could be detected. The n.m.r. spectrum showed only one peak in the cyclopentadienyl region, compared with the doublet for the rhenium hydride, and no peak due to a hydride. The compound was diamagnetic and molecular weight determinations showed the compound to be a dimer. It would appear therefore that the compound is $[(C_5H_5)_2Tc]_2$, presumably held together by a metal–metal bond as in the carbonyls. The contrast with the rhenium compound obtained under similar circumstances is noteworthy.

Cyclopentadienyl Carbonyl Compounds

Carbonylation of bis-π-cyclopentadienyl rhenium hydride.—Bis-π-cyclopentadienyl rhenium hydride reacted with carbon monoxide at 90° and 250 atmospheres pressure to give a yellow compound with the formula $C_{10}H_{11}Re(CO)_2$.[40] This compound melted at 111–112° and could be sublimed in a vacuum at 90–100°; it was diamagnetic with a dipole moment of 3.85 D. The compound was soluble in benzene and similar solvents, but it could be distinguished from bis-π-cyclopentadienyl rhenium hydride in acetone solution by its resistance to air oxidation. Molecular weight determinations in benzene showed it to be monomeric and on the basis of these measurements Fischer and Wirzmuller suggested structure I involving a σ-bonded cyclopentadiene ring and a hydridic proton between the metal and a π-cyclopentadiene ring.

Structure I

Later work[49] has shown this formulation to be incorrect on the basis of n.m.r. and infra-red studies. No peak due to a heavily shielded proton could be found in the n.m.r. spectrum and all proton resonances that were detected were assigned. In addition, examination of the sharp peak due to the π-cyclopentadienyl ring protons showed no evidence of splitting even under very high resolution, such as was found for bis-π-cyclopentadienyl rhenium hydride. the failure to observe such a splitting was regarded as further evidence that the new compound did not contain a metal hydrogen bond.

The infra-red spectra of compounds with σ-C_5H_5 groups show two peaks at about 3000 cm^{-1} due to this ring.[32] The spectrum of $C_{10}H_{11}Re(CO)_2$ showed six peaks in the carbon hydrogen region (see Table 7-12) in addition to the one at 3112 cm^{-1} which was assigned to the carbon–hydrogen stretches in the π-cyclopentadienyl ring.

The unsaturated nature of $C_{10}H_{11}Re(CO)_2$ was confirmed by the rapid decolourization of bromine in carbon tetrachloride to give an orange precipitate that was too unstable to be characterized.[49] The compound absorbed one mole of hydrogen on catalytic hydrogen whereas the original formulation would require two moles of hydrogen. Green and Wilkinson suggested that the compound must be formulated as π-cyclopentadienyl-(cyclopentadiene) rhenium dicarbonyl (structure II) and its hydrogenation product as π-cyclopentadienylcyclopentene rhenium dicarbonyl (structure III).

Structure II   Structure III

Since the compound $C_{10}H_{11}Re(CO)_2$ has, on the above evidence, neither a σ-cyclopentadiene ring nor a hydridic proton, it was necessary to assume that one of the double bonds in cyclopentadiene was acting as a donor in a manner similar to that of other olefin complexes with metals at the end of the transition series.[50] Part of the infra-red spectra of $C_{10}H_{11}Re(CO)_2$ and $C_{10}H_{13}Re(CO)_2$ are given in Table 7-12.

Table 7-12. Infra-red spectra of some π-cyclopentadienyl compounds of rhenium in CS_2 and CCl_4 solution

π-$C_5H_5Re(CO)_2C_5H_6$	π-$C_5H_5Re(CO)_2C_5H_8$	π-$C_5H_5Re(CO)_3$	Assignment
3112 w	3115 w	3117 w	1
3063 w	—	—	2
3025 m	3020 m	—	3
2954 m	2960 s	—	4
2931 m	2895 m	—	4
2871 s	2855 v.s.	—	4
2824 m	—	—	
1973 v.s.	1971 v.s.	2041 v.s.	5
1893 v.s.	1890 v.s.	1939 v.s.	5

Assignments: 1. C—H stretch in π-C_5H_5
2. H—C=C-H stretch
3. H—C=C-H stretch
4. > CH_2 stretch
5. —C—O stretch

K

A comparison of the spectra in Table 7-12 shows that the band at 3063 cm $^{-1}$ in $C_{10}H_{11}Re(CO)_2$ disappeared on hydrogenation whilst the band at 3025 cm $^{-1}$ was virtually unchanged. The band at 3063 cm $^{-1}$ was therefore assigned to the carbon–hydrogen stretch of the uncoordinated olefinic group, the band at 3025 cm $^{-1}$ in $C_{10}H_{11}Re(CO)_2$ and the one at 3020 cm $^{-1}$ in $C_{10}H_{13}Re(CO)_2$ were assigned to the carbon–hydrogen stretches of the coordinated olefin group, these values were in the same region as those previously reported for other olefin complexes.[50]

π-Cyclopentadienyl rhenium tricarbonyl.—An attempt[49] to prepare π-$C_5H_5Re(CO)_2C_5H_6$ directly from rhenium carbonyl and dicyclopentadiene under reflux led to the isolation of π-cyclopentadienyl rhenium tricarbonyl, $C_5H_5Re(CO)_3$ which was found to have properties very similar to its manganese analogue.[51] This same compound has also been isolated[52] by treating bis-π-cyclopentadienyl rhenium hydride (made *in situ* by the interaction of rhenium pentachloride and sodium cyclopentadienide in ethyleneglycoldimethyl ether, *diglyme*), with carbon monoxide at 225° and 48 atmospheres pressure for an hour, conditions very similar to those used for the preparation of $C_{10}H_{11}Re(CO)_2$. π-Cyclopentadienyl rhenium tricarbonyl is a white solid m.p. 111–114°. It is soluble in organic solvents and may be recrystallized from the lower paraffins.[52]

π-Cyclopentadienyl technetium tricarbonyl.—This compound has been briefly reported.[53] Technetium tetrachloride was converted to technetium pentacarbonyl chloride by treating with carbon monoxide under high pressure in the presence of copper which acts as a halogen acceptor. Treatment of the pentacarbonyl chloride with sodium cyclopentadienide gave π-cyclopentadienyl technetium tricarbonyl, m.p. 87.5°.

Arene Complexes

Arene complexes of rhenium.—Arene complexes of rhenium (I) have been obtained using benzene and mesitylene.[54] The cation $[Re(C_6H_6)_2]^+$ was isolated from the reaction products when rhenium pentachloride, aluminium chloride and aluminium were heated in a sealed tube at 130°. After reaction the tube was cooled, the solvent removed under vacuum and the contents of the tube were then carefully hydrolysed under nitrogen in ice cold water. The arene cation was stable to hydrolysis and could be isolated as its tetraphenylborate. The corresponding mesitylene complex was made in a similar way.

Arene complexes of technetium.—The dibenzene technetium (I) cation has been prepared in the same way as its rhenium analogue.[55] Technetium tetrachloride, aluminium, aluminium chloride and benzene were heated in a sealed tube at 135° for two days. After hydrolysis the cation was isolated as its hexafluorophosphate. X-ray diffraction studies showed it to be isomorphous with the corresponding rhenium compound.

Other Organometallic Compounds

Acetylene and olefin complexes of rhenium.—Very stable monomeric, diamagnetic acetylene complexes have been obtained directly from rhenium trichloride and triphenylphosphine rhenium trichloride.[56] For example, phenylacetylene gave $ReCl(C_6H_5C\equiv CH)_2$ with the trichloride. In these compounds the triple $C\equiv C$ bond is reduced effectively to a double $C=C$ bond as shown by the shift of the C–C stretching frequency to 1700 cm^{-1}. The acetylene may be regarded as bonded to the metal by two σ bonds from the carbon atoms adjacent to the multiple bond as suggested by Chatt and coworkers for the platinum acetylene complexes.[57]

Complexes have also been obtained from hydroxyacetylenes; thus, with but-l-yne-3-methyl-3-ol a compound of formula $ReCl(C_5H_8O)_2$ was obtained from the trichloride and $ReCl[P(C_6H_5)_3](C_5H_8O)_2$ from triphenylphosphine rhenium trichloride.[56] Again the bonding in these complexes was suggested to be similar to that in the analogous platinum compounds with the hydroxy acetylene acting as a bidentate group.[58]

Rhenium trichloride and triphenylphosphinerhenium trichloride reacted with dicyclopentadiene to give black insoluble $ReCl_2(C_{10}H_{12})_2$ and soluble $ReCl[P(C_6H_5)_3](C_{10}H_{12})_2$ respectively. Nothing is known of the constitution of these compounds.

Rhenium trimethyl.—Druce[59] reported that rhenium trichloride reacted vigorously with methyl magnesium iodide in ether solution. After acid hydrolysis a yellow ethereal layer was separated and dried. Distillation gave a colourless liquid which had a rhenium content close to that required for rhenium trimethyl. Later attempts[60, 61] to repeat this work have been unsuccessful and the existence of a simple alkyl derivative of rhenium is very doubtful.

References

1. W. HIEBER and H. FUCHS, *Z. Anorg. Allgem. Chem.* **248**, 256 (1941).
2. F. A. COTTON, A. LIEHR and G. WILKINSON, *J. Inorg. Nucl. Chem.* **2**, 141 (1956).
3. L. F. DAHL, E. ISHISHI and R. E. RUNDLE, *J. Chem. Phys.* **26**, 1750 (1957).
4. R. COLTON, J. DALZIEL, W. P. GRIFFITH and G. WILKINSON, *J. Chem. Soc.* 71 (1960).
5. J. C. HILEMAN, D. K. HUGGINS and H. D. KAESZ, *J. Am. Chem. Soc.* **83**, 2953 (1961).
6. W. HIEBER and C. HERGET, *Angew. Chem.* **73**, 579 (1961).

7. M. D. WALLACH, *Acta Cryst.* **15**, 1058 (1962).
8. H. D. KAESZ and D. K. HUGGINS, *Can. J. Chem.* **41**, 1250 (1963).
9. W. HIEBER and G. BRAUN, *Z. Naturforsch.* **14B**, 132 (1959).
10. W. BECK, W. HIEBER and G. BRAUN, *Z. Anorg. Allgem. Chem.* **308**, 23 (1961).
11. J. C. HILEMAN, D. K. HUGGINS and H. D. KAESZ, *Inorg. Chem.* **1**, 933 (1962).
12. W. HIEBER and H. SCHULTEN, *Z. Anorg. Allgem. Chem.* **243**, 164 (1939).
13. W. HIEBER, R. SCHUH and H. FUCHS, *Z. Anorg. Allgem. Chem.* **248**, 243 (1941).
14. E. W. ABEL, G. B. HARGREAVES and G. WILKINSON, *J. Chem. Soc.* 3149 (1959).
15. E. O. BRIMM, M. A. LYNCH and W. SESNEY, *J. Am. Chem. Soc.* **76**, 3831 (1954).
16. R. SCHUH, *Z. Anorg. Allgem. Chem.* **248**, 276 (1941).
17. W. HIEBER and H. FUCHS, *Z. Anorg. Allgem. Chem.* **248**, 269 (1941).
18. G. WILKINSON, personal communication.
19. E. W. ABEL and G. WILKINSON, *J. Chem. Soc.* 1501 (1959).
20. J. CHATT, L. A. DUNCANSON and L. M. VENANZI, *J. Chem. Soc.* 4456 (1955).
21. L. ORGEL, *J. Inorg. Nucl. Chem.* **2**, 137 (1956).
22. M. FRENI and V. VALENTI, *J. Inorg. Nucl. Chem.* **16**, 240 (1961).
23. W. HIEBER and L. SCHUSTER, *Z. Anorg. Allgem. Chem.* **287**, 214 (1956).
24. W. HIEBER and L. SCHUSTER, *Z. Anorg. Allgem. Chem.* **285**, 205 (1956).
25. W. HIEBER and T. KRUCK, *Z. Naturforsch.* **16B**, 709 (1961).
26. W. HIEBER and T. KRUCK, *Angew. Chem.* **73**, 580 (1961).
27. W. HIEBER, G. BRAUN and W. BECK, *Chem. Ber.* **93**, 901 (1960).
28. H. D. KAESZ, R. B. KING and F. G. A. STONE, *Z. Naturforsch.* **15b**, 763 (1960).
29. W. BECK, W. HIEBER and H. TENGLER, *Chem. Ber.* **94**, 862 (1961).
30. G. WILKINSON and J. M. BIRMINGHAM, *J. Am. Chem. Soc.* **77**, 3421 (1955).
31. M. L. H. GREEN, L. PRATT and G. WILKINSON, *J. Chem. Soc.* 3916 (1958).
32. T. S. PIPER and G. WILKINSON, *J. Inorg. Nucl. Chem.* **3**, 104 (1956).
33. R. A. FRIEDAL, I. WENDER, S. L. SHUFLER and H. W. STERNBERG, *J. Am. Chem. Soc.* **77**, 3951 (1955).
34. F. A. COTTON and G. WILKINSON, *Chem. Ind. London* 1305 (1956).
35. J. CHATT, L. A. DUNCANSON and B. L. SHAW, *Proc. Chem. Soc.* 343 (1957).
36. L. FRIEDMAN, A. P. IRSA and G. WILKINSON, *J. Am. Chem. Soc.* **77**, 3689 (1955).
37. J. R. WHITE and A. E. CAMERON, *Phys. Rev.* **74**, 991 (1948).
38. G. WILKINSON, *Proceedings of the Sixth International Conference on Co-ordination Chemistry*, Detroit (1961).
39. G. WILKINSON, J. M. BIRMINGHAM and F. A. COTTON, *J. Inorg. Nucl. Chem.* **2**, 95 (1956).
40. E. O. FISCHER and A. WIRZMULLER, *Z. Naturforsch.* **12b**, 737 (1957).
41. R. WEST, *J. Am. Chem. Soc.* **79**, 4568 (1957).
42. T. C. WADDINGTON, *J. Chem. Soc.* 1708 (1958).
43. D. W. A. SHARP, *J. Chem. Soc.* 2558 (1958).
44. P. RUMPF, G. GERAULT-VEXLEARSEHIM and R. SCHAAL, *Bull. Soc. Chim. France* **554** (1955).
45. A. D. LIEHR, *Naturwiss* **44**, 61 (1957).
46. L. D. DAVE, D. F. EVANS and G. WILKINSON, *J. Chem. Soc.* 3684 (1959).
47. H. S. GUTOWSKY, D. M. McCALL and C. P. SLICHTER, *J. Chem. Phys.* **21**, 279 (1953).

48. D. K. HUGGINS and H. D. KAESZ, *J. Am. Chem. Soc.* **83**, 4474 (1961).
49. M. L. H. GREEN and G. WILKINSON, *J. Chem. Soc.* 4314 (1958).
50. J. CHATT and L. M. VENANZI, *J. Chem. Soc.* 4735 (1957).
51. T. S. PIPER and G. WILKINSON, *J. Inorg. Nucl. Chem.* **1**, 165 (1955).
52. R. L. PRUETT and G. L. MOREHOUSE, *Chem. Ind. London* 980 (1958).
53. C. PALM, E. O. FISCHER and F. BAUMGAERNTNER, *Naturwiss* **49**, 279 (1962).
54. E. O. FISCHER and A. WIRZMULLER, *Chem. Ber.* **90**, 1725 (1957).
55. C. PALM, E. O. FISCHER and F. BAUMGAERNTNER, *Tetrahedron Letters* 253 (1962).
56. R. COLTON, R. LEVITUS and G. WILKINSON, *Nature* **186**, 233 (1960).
57. J. CHATT, L. A. DUNCANSON and R. G. GUY, *Chem. Ind. London* 430 (1959).
58. J. CHATT, L. A. DUNCANSON and R. G. GUY, *Nature* **184**, 526 (1959).
59. J. G. F. DRUCE, *J. Chem. Soc.* 1129 (1934).
60. H. GILMAN, R. G. JONES, F. W. MOORE and M. J. KOLBEZEN, *J. Am. Chem. Soc.* **63**, 2525 (1941).
61. R. COLTON and G. WILKINSON, Unpublished observations.

8

Cyanide and Thiocyanate Complexes

Rhenium forms an extensive series of cyanide complexes. True complex cyanides have been claimed for every oxidation state between zero and six, with the exception of Re^{IV}. Several mixed complexes such as nitrosylcyanides, and hydroxycyanides are also known. In its five and six valent complexes rhenium has a strong tendency towards eight coordination. Few technetium cyanides have so far been reported.

Cyanide Complexes of Rhenium

There is some confusion concerning the cyanide complexes of Re^O and Re^I. A compound thought to be potassium hexacyanorhenate(0), $K_6Re(CN)_6$, was isolated as a yellow insoluble product of the exhaustive reduction of potassium hexachlororhenate(IV) by potassium amalgam under an atmosphere of nitrogen.[1] Analysis showed a ratio of potassium to rhenium of approximately 6:1 and the compound was said to oxidize more readily than the better established complex of Re^I. However, until the preparation has been repeated and the formulation supported by magnetic susceptibility data and other physical measurements the identity of the compound must be open to some doubt.

The existence of cyanide complexes of Re^I is better established. Clauss and Lissner[1] reported the isolation of the trihydrate of potassium hexacyanorhenate(I) as the major product of the reduction of potassium hexachlororhenate(IV) by potassium amalgam. A very weak paramagnetism was observed, which was ascribed to impurities, and the result was taken to confirm the presence of Re^I. Solutions of the complex were stable when alkaline, but acidification led to evolution of hydrogen cyanide. Clauss and Lissner[1] showed that the anhydrous compound, prepared by drying the hydrate over phosphorus pentoxide, had a face-centred cubic

140

lattice with $a = 12.05 \pm 0.02$ Å. This has recently been confirmed by Schwochau and Herr[2] who also prepared the corresponding technetium compound and showed that the cyanide complexes of Mn^I; Tc^I and Re^I are isostructural.

Recently anhydrous potassium hexacyanorhenate(I) was said to be the major product of the reduction of potassium hexachlororhenate(IV) by potassium borohydride in the presence of excess potassium cyanide.[3] The oxidation number of the rhenium in the compound was shown to be one, but the reported analyses showed errors of the order of 10–12% in the potassium and cyanide figures and a smaller error in the rhenium analysis when compared with the theoretical value for the hexacyanorhenate(I). Examination of the results shows that the figures fit much better for potassium hexacyanorhenate(0), $K_6Re(CN)_6$. The reported cyanide result is about 2% low for the zero valent compound, but the complete analysis totalled only 98.5% and it is not unreasonable to assume that the cyanide analysis is the least accurate. If the cyanide figure is corrected assuming the *missing* fraction is due to cyanide the results in Table 8-1 are obtained.

Table 8-1. Analysis of rhenium cyanide complexes

	Calc. for $K_5Re(CN)_6$	Calc. for $K_6Re(CN)_6$	Reported*
K	36.34	40.58	40.20
Re	34.64	32.23	33.12
CN	29.02	27.16	25.06 (26.68**)

* Mean of two sets of independent values.
** Corrected as described in text.

It is clear that the analytical figures favour the zero valent compound. The finding of an oxidation number of + 1 for rhenium may indicate the presence of an unsuspected hydridic proton giving a cyanide hydride of Re^I, $K_6[ReH(CN)_6]$. This is particularly likely as borohydride was used as the reducing agent in this system. A similar solid whose analysis was much more nearly correct for potassium hexacyanorhenate(I) was obtained by the borohydride reduction of potassium tetracyanodioxorhenate(IV) in the presence of excess potassium cyanide.[3] Further investigation of these systems is desirable.

The stablization of Re^I by cyanide ligands has been conclusively demonstrated by polarographic studies[4, 5] on the reduction of various rhenium compounds in cyanide solutions. These results are discussed in chapter 9.

The preparation of potassium hexacyanorhenate(II) has been briefly reported.[6] It is formed by refluxing the well-known aquopentacyanorhenate(II) with aqueous potassium cyanide solution. The original violet-brown solution turned orange, and brown crystals of the trihydrate of potassium hexacyanorhenate(II), $K_4Re(CH)_6 \cdot 3H_2O$, were isolated.

Potassium hexacyanorhenate(III), $K_3Re(CN)_6$, was isolated as a green compound by reducing potassium octacyanorhenate(V) with potassium borohydride.[7] The potassium salt was not isolated in this case and the anion was precipitated as the hexammine cobaltic salt which had a magnetic moment of 2.6 B.M. at room temperature, consistent with the two inpaired electrons expected for this complex. Meier and Treadwell[8] reported that rhenium trichloride reacted with potassium cyanide solution giving a remarkable series of colour changes. These observations were later confirmed,[7] the initial red solution changed to blue on warming, then quickly changed to green and finally after several days in the presence of a large excess of potassium cyanide the solution became yellowish brown. The final product was shown to be potassium octacyanorhenate(V), but by addition of a large excess of potassium hydroxide to the intermediate green stage small amounts of potassium hexacyanorhenate(III) were isolated.[7]

Potassium octacyanorhenate(V) has been prepared by the action of potassium cyanide on potassium hexaiodorhenate(IV) in hot methanol solution[7, 9], the brown diamagnetic complex precipitated and excess potassium cyanide was extracted by methanol. Alternatively, the monohydrate of the complex cyanide could be isolated by recrystallizing the crude product from water.[7] The compound is stable in water and alkaline solutions, giving yellowish brown solutions when dilute and reddish brown solutions when more concentrated. In general acid solutions of potassium octacyanorhenate(V) are unstable in the presence of air, and nitric acid reacts with it to give a nitrosyl cyanide complex.

The infra-red spectrum of potassium octacyanorhenate(V) in Nujol mulls showed three cyanide stretching frequencies at 2140, 2100 and 2050 cm^{-1}, a spectrum very similar to those of the molybdenum and tungsten octacyanides. In aqueous solution however, the compound showed only one peak (as does the octacyanomolybdate(IV) anion) at 2100 cm^{-1}, suggesting that the splitting in the solid state spectra is due to crystal interaction. It seems therefore that the octacyanide complexes of rhenium have the same duodecahedral structure as the molybdenum complexes.[10]

Treatment of potassium octacyanorhenate(V) solution with dilute hydrochloric, acetic or perchloric acids in the presence of air yielded a purple solution,[7] this colour change occurred only in the presence of oxygen when the pH of the solution was reduced below pH 5. There was no reaction with oxygen in basic solution. A potassium salt could not be isolated from the purple solution, but immediate addition of hexammine cobaltic chloride gave an insoluble purple precipitate which was shown to be the hexammine cobaltic salt of the octacyanorhenate (VI) anion, $[Co(NH_3)_6]_2[Re(CN)_8]_3$.[7] The gross reaction was therefore

$$2 [Re(CN)_8]^{3-} + \tfrac{1}{2} O_2 + 2 H^+ \rightarrow 2 [Re(CN)_8]^{2-} + H_2O.$$

Since the octacyanorhenate (V) was diamagnetic the octacyanorhenate (VI) should be paramagnetic with one unpaired electron. The magnetic moment of the insoluble hexammine cobaltic salt was indeed 2.0 B.M. (at room temperature) but the behaviour of the octacyanorhenate (VI) anion in solution was unusual. When an aqueous solution of potassium octacyanorhenate (V) was made faintly acid with hydrochloric acid, the purple solution contained a paramagnetic species as expected but this rapidly became diamagnetic without any apparent colour change. The change in susceptibility was exponential with a half-life of 5 ± 2 seconds. A log plot allowed extrapolation back to zero time (addition of acid), the moment at zero time was found to be 2.0 B.M. agreeing with the moment of the hexammine cobaltic salt.

If hexammine cobaltic chloride was added to the potassium octacyanorhenate (VI) solution immediately after the addition of the acid, the whole of the purple species was precipitated from the solution. On the other hand, if the solution was kept for some time, and hence allowed to become diamagnetic before addition of the hexammine cobaltic chloride, only a small amount of precipitate (about 5% of that expected) was obtained.[7]

Tetraphenylarsonium chloride also gave a purple precipitate with potassium octacyanorhenate (VI) solution.[7] If precipitated immediately the solid was paramagnetic with a magnetic moment of 2.0 B.M. If the solution was allowed to become diamagnetic before the reagent was added, the whole of the purple species still precipitated but in this case the magnetic susceptibility of the solid was very low. It was found that about 95% of this solid could be dissolved in and recrystallized from acetone, this fraction was diamagnetic but the remaining 5% of the original precipitate insoluble in acetone was paramagnetic with a magnetic moment of 2.0 B.M. Analysis of both samples corresponded to tetraphenylarsonium octacyanorhenate (VI), $[(C_6H_5)_4As]_2Re(CN)_8$.

These reactions may suggest that there was an equilibrium in the solutions between two species (95% diamagnetic and 5% paramagnetic). However, if this were so the addition of hexammine cobaltic chloride should displace the equilibrium to the paramagnetic side since it precipitates only this species. In actual fact when hexammine cobaltic chloride was added to the aged purple solution, there was a small amount of paramagnetic precipitate formed immediately and then no more.

High-resolution nuclear magnetic resonance studies on an anhydrous acetone solution of the diamagnetic tetraphenylarsonium salt showed the absence of any peak in the characteristic metal–hydride region, but a peak was observed on the low-field side relative to water in the region where protons of soluble metal hydroxides show resonances. The gradual addition of traces of water to the acetone solution caused the peak to broaden and then finally disappear, suggesting that exchange was taking place between the water and the protons causing the peak.

To explain these results it was suggested that the diamagnetic species is obtained by further oxidation, and that the rhenium is utilizing its remaining $5d$ orbital to form a 9-coordinate hydroxycyanide complex $[Re^{VII}(CN)_8OH]^{2-}$. The presence of one hydroxyl group cannot be detected in a compound of molecular weight about 1200 by conventional analytical techniques, but it would be difficult to account for the diamagnetism of the species and the peak in the n.m.r. spectrum without the presence of the hydroxyl group. That there are still eight cyanide groups attached to the rhenium in the aged purple solutions is shown by the nearly quantitative reduction of these solutions to potassium octacyanorhenate(v) by sodium borohydride.[7]

Some of the reactions described above are summarized in the following scheme

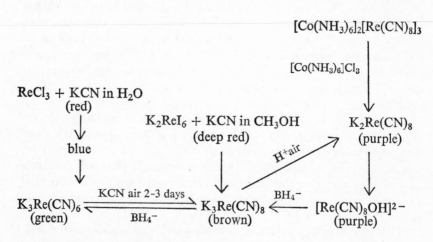

Mixed Cyanides of Rhenium

Mixed cyanide complexes such as oxycyanides, aquocyanides andnitrosyl-cyanides are known for a number of different oxidation states of rhenium. In many cases these compounds may be regarded as simple substitution products of the true cyanide complexes.

Sodium pentacyanoaquorhenate(II) has been prepared by the reduction of sodium perrhenate by sodium amalgam in the presence of excess sodium cyanide.[11] On gradual addition of the amalgam the solution first turned green then to a much darker green. After reduction was complete the solution was acidified with acetic acid and CO_2-free air was bubbled through the solution to remove the liberated hydrogen cyanide. The solution was then neutralized with sodium hydroxide and the cyano complex was separated as an oil by addition of alcohol to the solution. The oil was dissolved in a little water and the alcohol separation was then repeated several times. The final oil was dried over phosphorus pentoxide to give sodium pentacyanoaquorhenate(II).

The compound is extremely hygroscopic and dissolves in water to give a brown solution. On boiling with dilute mineral acids it gives a violet colour which slowly fades. The valency state of the rhenium in the complex was determined by oxidation with chromate solution in the usual way.

Heating sodium pentacyanoaquorhenate(II) in an atmosphere of carbon monoxide at 140° gave the corresponding pentacyanocarbonylrhenate(II), $Na[Re(CN)_5CO]$. This compound is an extremely hygroscopic blue substance, the solid and its cold aqueous solutions are quite stable but on boiling the solution decomposes apparently reforming the aquo complex.[12]

6 M nitric acid reacted with sodium pentacyanoaquorhenate(II) to give a red solution.[13] After completion of the reaction the solution was evaporated to dryness and the solid extracted with methanol to give a red crystalline hygroscopic complex. Solutions of this compound gave a pink precipitate with silver nitrate which analysis showed to be silver pentacyanonitrosylrhenate(II), $Ag_2[ReNO(CN)_5]$. The formula of the compound suggests that the nitric oxide is present as the NO^+ group but this has not been confirmed by an infra-red study nor have magnetic studies been made of any of the Re^{II} mixed cyanides described here.

Oxidation of sodium pentacyanoaquorhenate(II) solution by bromine changed the colour of the solution from violet-brown to deep green and sodium pentacyanoaquorhenate(III), $Na_2[Re(CN)_5H_2O]$, could be isolated from the solution.[14] The rhenium(III) complex is soluble in alcohol and this forms the basis of separation from the corresponding rhenium(II) complex which is insoluble in alcohol. Analysis of the green solid showed a ratio of rhenium : nitrogen = 1:5 and the trivalency of the metal was proved by chromate oxidation. Heavy metal cations gave insoluble precipitates with the complex anion. Rather surprisingly sodium pentacyanoaquorhenate(III) was found to be quite a good oxidizing agent, for example it liberated iodine from potassium iodide, and its solutions were unstable, especially in light.

Potassium tricyanotrihydroxyrhenate(III) has been prepared by the borohydride reduction of potassium tetracyanodioxorhenate(IV) in both the presence or absence of excess potassium cyanide.[3] About 17 hours after the addition of borohydride to a solution of the rhenium(IV) compound the solution had become an intense opaque blue colour. On pouring the aqueous solution into ethanol a blue precipitate was obtained which was extracted by methanol for 2 days to remove excess cyanide. Analysis indicated that the compound was potassium tricyanotrihydroxyrhenate(III), $K_3[Re(CN)_3(OH)_3]$. It may be that this blue compound is the intermediate mentioned earlier as occurring in the reaction between rhenium trichloride and potassium cyanide. However in this case the blue compound rapidly reacts with further cyanide to form the hexacyano complex. It is rather surprising that a trihydroxy complex can be isolated in the presence of excess cyanide ion with no further reaction and even more surprising that hydroxyl can actually displace a cyanide ligand from the rhenium(IV) cyanocomplex starting material. It is unfortunate that no infra-red study was made on this compound to confirm the absence of rhenium–oxygen double bonds, aquo groups or even possibly metal–hydrogen bonds. In addition magnetic studies on both of the reported rhenium(III) mixed cyanides would be useful.

Addition of a solution of potassium hexachlororhenate(IV) to potassium cyanide solution gave a white precipitate initially, but this rapidly disappeared as the solution turned black.[3] A greyish black solid was precipitated on pouring the aqueous solution into alcohol. This was separated and extracted with methanol for up to 5 days until a fresh extract showed no evidence of cyanide ion. Analysis showed the compound to be potassium tetracyanodioxorhenate(IV), $K_4[ReO_2(CN)_4]$, but again no physical measurements were made to substantiate the formula. Since a neutral solution of potassium hexachlororhenate(IV) was used in the preparation and potassium cyanide solutions are distinctly alkaline it would appear that the first stage of the reaction is hydrolysis of the chlorocomplex to hydrated rhenium dioxide which then reacts with potassium cyanide to form the observed complex. This mechanism would explain why the final product contained no chlorine. It is interesting to note that potassium cyanide dissolves rhenium dioxide in the presence of an oxidizing agent to form potassium tetracyanodioxorhenate(V), $K_3[ReO_2(CN)_4]$, but no observations appear to have been made on this reaction in the absence of an oxidizing agent.

Potassium tetracyanodioxorhenate(V) is one of the better known complex compounds of rhenium. It is usually prepared by dissolving hydrated rhenium dioxide in aqueous potassium cyanide solution in the presence of hydrogen peroxide.[15, 16] The red complex is precipitated by pouring the aqueous solution into alcohol and finally recrystallized from water.

Potassium tetracyanodioxorhenate(v) is a stable diamagnetic red solid, its crystal structure has been determined.[17] The compound is triclinic with the following dimensions

$$a = 7.73 \pm 0.02 \text{ Å} \quad \alpha = 107°28' \pm 10'$$
$$b = 7.35 \pm 0.02 \text{ Å} \quad \beta = 108°28' \pm 10'$$
$$c = 6.32 \pm 0.02 \text{ Å} \quad \gamma = 114°20' \pm 10'$$

The unit cell contains one formula unit.

Cyanide Complexes of Technetium

A comparison[4] of the reduction of potassium pertechnetate and potassium perrhenate in cyanide media suggested that cyanide would stabilize Tc^{IV} and not Tc^V in sharp contrast to the behaviour of rhenium which is stabilized strongly in the pentavalent state by cyanide. It is noteworthy that so far no cyanocompound of Tc^V has been prepared.

The reaction of potassium hexaiodotechnate(IV) with potassium cyanide in methanol has been investigated on a semimicro scale only.[18] A reddish brown flocculent precipitate was formed immediately on mixing solutions of the reactants. The complex was shown to be paramagnetic by the n.m.r. method[19] and it was also shown to hydrolyse fairly readily. These are properties which would be expected for potassium hexacyano-technate(IV) formed by direct replacement of iodine by cyanide but they are not the properties expected for potassium octacyanotechnate(V) which would be the observed product if technetium behaved in the same way as rhenium.

Potassium hexacyanotechnate(I), $K_5Tc(CN)_6$, has been prepared by the reduction of potassium pertechnetate or potassium tetracyanotrihydroxy-technate(IV) by potassium amalgam in the presence of excess potassium cyanide.[2] The olive-green complex was found to have a face-centred cubic lattice ($a = 12.106 \pm 0.001$ Å) isostructural with the corresponding manganese and rhenium compounds.

Potassium tetracyanotrihydroxytechnate(IV) has been prepared by the dissolution of technetium dioxide in potassium cyanide solution.[20] The complex anion was isolated as the thallium salt, $Tl_3[Tc(OH)_3(CN)_4]$, which crystallizes with a low symmetry lattice. Schwochau and Herr[20] were aware of the possibility that the complex may be thallium tetracyanooxo-hydroxytechnate(IV), $Tl_3[TcO(OH)(CN)_4]$, and their infra-red spectrum of the compound is not inconsistent with this formulation. No matter which of these formulae proves to be the correct one the difference between the reaction of rhenium and technetium in these systems is noteworthy.

Thiocyanate Complexes of Rhenium

The position regarding thiocyanate complexes of rhenium is confusing. It has been known for many years that a red colour is formed when perrhenate ion is reduced by a variety of reagents in the presence of potassium thiocyanate. Although the colour has been widely used as the basis of a colourimetric method of analysis for rhenium, little is known of the structure of the complex. Indeed, there has been so much controversy, and so many oxidation states of rhenium in the complex have been suggested, that it appears likely that there is in fact more than one complex. The similar technetium system has been shown to contain two species.[21]

The thiocyanate complex formed in hydrochloric acid solutions by the action of stannous chloride on potassium perrhenate is red. It is easily extracted into ether or chloroform and it is fairly readily oxidized to Re^{VII} by hydrogen peroxide.

Tarayan and Ekimyan[22] studied the reduction of potassium perrhenate in 3–5 M hydrochloric acid with varying amounts of Ti^{III} salts. The course of the reaction was followed spectrophotometrically and the maximum optical density occurred when three equivalents of reductant were added, suggesting that the thiocyanate complex contained Re^{IV}.

Tribalat[23] used potentiometric and colourimetric methods to determine the valence state of the rhenium in the red complex. It was found that in 1 M hydrochloric acid 2.5 equivalents of stannous chloride were required to obtain maximum colour. In more concentrated solutions of hydrochloric acid even less stannous chloride was required. Tribalat concluded that the rhenium in the complex had an average oxidation number of 4.5.

Holeman[24] found the oxidation number of the rhenium to be variable but about 5. Druce[25] believed the complex to contain Re^{VI} and the formula suggested was $ReO(SCN)_4$.

Recent work[26] has shown that the complex is anionic and it has been suggested that the formula is $K_3[ReO_2(SCH)_4]$ analogous to the well-known oxycyanide of Re^V but no evidence definitely confirming this formulation has been reported. It is unlikely that a compound of this type would be soluble in ether and chloroform. The question of the constitution of the red thiocyanate complexes of rhenium is obviously still far from being settled.

The only other thiocyanate complexes reported are a series of hexathiocyanatorhenate(IV) compounds whose magnetic properties have been reported by Nelson and coworkers.[27] The magnetic data are summarized in Table 8-2. The compounds obeyed the Curie–Weiss Law and were generally similar in their magnetic behaviour to the hexahalorhenates (IV). Unfortunately no details of the preparation of these compounds was given, and no other mention of these compounds appears in the literature. Judging by the magnetic behaviour the compounds appear to be genuine. The most likely preparation would probably be the action of potassium thiocyanate on potassium hexaiodorhenate(IV) in some organic solvent. If this is the case the difference between the behaviour of cyanide and thiocyanate in this reaction is noteworthy.

Table 8-2. Magnetic properties of the hexathiocyanatorhenates(IV)

	θ	μ_{eff} 300° (B.M.)
$K_2Re(SCN)_6$	149°	3.6
$Ag_2Re(SCN)_6$	212°	3.9
$Tl_2Re(SCN)_6$	41°	3.6

References

1. D. CLAUSS and A. LISSNER, *Z. Anorg. Allgem. Chem.* **297**, 300 (1958).
2. K. SCHWOCHAU and W. HERR, *Z. Anorg. Allgem. Chem.* **319**, 148 (1962).
3. P. H. L. WALTER, J. KLEINBERG, and E. GRISWOLD, *Inorg. Chem.* **1**, 10 (1962).
4. R. COLTON, J. DALZIEL, W. P. GRIFFITH and G. WILKINSON, *J. Chem. Soc.* 71 (1960).
5. B. JEZOWSKA-TRZEBIATOWSKA, *Chem. Tech. Berlin* **9**, 470 (1957).
6. S. SEN, *Sci. Cult. Calcutta* **26**, 139 (1960).
7. R. COLTON, R. D. PEACOCK and G. WILKINSON, *J. Chem. Soc.* 1374 (1960).
8. J. MEIER and W. D. TREADWELL, *Helv. Chim. Acta* **38**, 1679 (1955).
9. R. COLTON, R. D. PEACOCK and G. WILKINSON, *Nature* **182**, 393 (1958).
10. J. L. HOARD and H. H. NORDSIECK, *J. Am. Chem. Soc.* **61**, 2853 (1939).
11. S. SEN, *Sci. Cult. Calcutta* **23**, 664 (1958).
12. P. BANDYOPADHYAY, *Sci. Cult. Calcutta* **25**, 278 (1959).
13. B. K. SEN and P. B. SARKAR, *Sci. Cult. Calcutta* **27**, 404 (1961).
14. S. SEN, *Sci. Cult. Calcutta* **25**, 272 (1959).
15. W. KLEMM and G. FRISCHMUTH, *Z. Anorg. Allgem. Chem.* **230**, 215 (1937).
16. G. T. MORGAN and G. R. DAVIS, *J. Chem. Soc.* **1858** (1938).
17. K. LUKASZEWICZ and T. GLOWIAK, *Bull. Acad. Polon. Sci. Ser. Sci. Chim.* **9**, 613 (1961).
18. R. COLTON and G. WILKINSON, Unpublished observations.
19. D. F. EVANS, *J. Chem. Soc.* 2003 (1959).
20. K. SCHWOCHAU and W. HERR, *Z. Anorg. Allgem. Chem.* **318**, 198 (1962).
21. E. CROUTHAMEL, *Anal. Chem.* **29**, 1756 (1957).
22. V. M. TARAYAN and M. G. EKIMYAN, *Dokl. Akad. Nauk. S.S.S.R.* **27**, 33 (1958).
23. S. TRIBALAT, *Compt. rendus.* **223**, 34 (1946).
24. H. HOLEMAN, *Z. Anorg. Allgem. Chem.* **235**, 1 (1937).
25. J. G. F. DRUCE, *Rhenium*, Cambridge University Press (1948).
26. D. I. RYABCHIKOV, V. A. ZARINSKII and I. I. NAZARENKO, *Zh. Neorgan. Khim.* **6**, 641 (1961).
27. C. M. NELSON, G. E. BOYD and W. T. SMITH, JNR., *J. Am. Chem. Soc.* **76**, 348 (1954).

9

The Polarographic Reduction of Rhenium and Technetium Compounds and a Discussion of the Rhenide State

Not a great deal of effort has been directed towards a study of the polarographic reduction of rhenium compounds, and in most studies so far the perrhenate ion has been the starting material.

Calculations of the number of electrons involved in polarographic reduction are made using the Ilkovic equation.[3]

$$i_d = 603 \; n \; c \; D^{1/2} \; m^{2/3} \; t^{1/6}$$

where i_d is the diffusion-controlled limiting current.

n is the number of electrons involved in the reduction.

c is the concentration.

D is the diffusion coefficient of the ion being reduced.

m and t are constants for a particular dropping electrode used under fixed conditions.

These symbols and the symbol $E_{1/2}$ for the half-wave potential of a wave will be used throughout this chapter.

Rhenium can be determined polarographically and mention will be made of this in the chapter on analysis but in most cases the polarographic work has been carried out to show which valency states are stabilized by various ligands. Among the supporting electrolytes which have been studied are potassium hydroxide, hydrochloric, sulphuric and perchloric acids and potassium cyanide. In these media the results obtained are explicable and not unexpected but this can hardly be said to be the case in the reduction of potassium perrhenate in the presence of potassium chloride as supporting electrolyte. Under these conditions potassium perrhenate gives, on applying the Ilkovic equation, an n value of eight, implying a reduction to Re^{-1}, the so-called rhenide ion.

Subsequent preparative work has shown that the simple picture of a rhenide ion is untenable and that the rhenide state consists of one or more complex rhenium hydrides. Since much of the experimental evidence connected with the rhenides is contradictory and the issue is far from settled, an attempt will be made in this chapter to present all the presently available data.

Reduction of Perrhenate and Pertechnetate Ions

Perrhenate ion in hydrochloric and perchloric acids.—Lingane[1] found that potassium perrhenate gave only slight indications of a wave in 0.1 M hydrochloric acid but that as the acidity was increased a well-defined wave could be obtained. With constant perrhenate ion concentrations the wave height increased with acid concentrations up to about 2 M and then remained constant wiih increasing acidity, but below 2 M the wave was distorted by a rounded maximum which made the diffusion current ill-defined.

By applying the Ilkovic equation for solutions in 2–4 M hydrochloric acid, Lingane obtained a value of $n = 3$, that is reduction of Re^{VII} to Re^{IV}. Since the hexachlororhenate(IV) ion, $ReCl_6^{2-}$, is known to be stable under these conditions, Lingane suggested that the reduction proceeds to this ion. The half-wave potential for the reduction varies somewhat with the acidity being -0.45 v in 2 M hydrochloric acid and -0.31 v in 4.2 M acid. The small slope of the waves suggested that the reduction did not take place reversibly in a thermodynamic sense and thus the reversible potential of the reaction is more positive (greater oxidizing ability) than these values would indicate.

Similar, but much better defined waves were obtained by using perchloric acid instead of hydrochloric. The diffusion current was found to be proportional to the perrhenate ion concentration with a calculated value $n = 3$. The half-wave potential of the wave in 4 M perchloric acid showed a definite shift to more positive values as the perrhenate ion concentration was decreased indicating that the reduction was irreversible.

Objections to the interpretation of a three electron reduction from Re^{VII} to Re^{IV} have been raised by Rulfs and Elving,[2] who suggested that the wave was not diffusion-controlled and hence the Ilkovic equation could not be applied. They found that although the initial current step varies with the height of the mercury reservoir as expected for a diffusion-controlled process,[3] the temperature coefficient of the wave was zero or even slightly negative. Potassium perrhenate showed a normal temperature effect for conductivity so they claimed that a value of $n = 3$ would only be obtained at 25°.

Rulfs and Elving also suggested that the coulometric reduction of potassium perrhenate in acid media shows that a simple electron process

L

is not valid. Reduction in 4 M perchloric acid at 25° and potential settings of − 0.45 to − 0.55 v always gave rise to a continuous process. In a typical run at − 0.52 v reduction continued till the coulometer showed a volume of gas equal to seven times the theoretical amount for a three equivalent reduction and there was no indication of a falling off of the rate of gas evolution. Titration of the cell solution indicated that the rhenium had been reduced by only 0.2 equivalents, hence gas evolution at the mercury interface played a major part in the current consumption.

Pertechnetate ion in hydrochloric and perchloric acids.—Potassium pertechnetate (0.130 mM) in 4 M hydrochloric acid was also found to undergo reduction to the + 4 state[4] but a double wave was obtained corresponding to a one- and a two-electron reduction respectively. The waves were rather poorly defined with half wave potentials of − 0.52 v and − 0.68 v (*vs* s.c.e.) respectively. Both waves were shown to be irreversible.

Potassium pertechnetate showed no reduction in 4 M perchloric acid; the current merely gradually increased to the voltage of the reduction of the supporting electrolyte. This behaviour is very different from that of rhenium and so far no adequate explanation has been suggested to account for this difference.

Perrhenate and pertechnetate ions in potassium hydroxide.—Potassium perrhenate in 0.1 M potassium hydroxide gave a large poorly defined wave.[4] The n values calculated from the Ilkovic equation were not constant but varied with concentration, as they also did when potassium chloride was the supporting electrolyte. However, it seems that perrhenate ion is reduced to Re^{-1} rhenide in 0.1 M potassium hydroxide. The experimental results are given in Table 9-1.

Table 9-1. Polarographic reduction of perrhenate ion in 0.1 M potassium hydroxide[4]

Concn.	(mM)	1.01	0.71	0.49
i_d	(μA)	48.0	34.5	18.0
n		9.8	8.3	7.6
$E_{1/2}$	(v)	− 1.72	− 1.68	− 1.66

In contrast to rhenium, potassium pertechnetate is reduced only to the + 4 state in two stages corresponding to a two- and a one-electron reduction at − 0.85 and − 1.15 v respectively.[4] The waves, especially the first one, are well defined and there is no variation of n value with concentration. Both technetium waves were found to be irreversible. The experimental results are shown in Table 9-2.

Table 9-2. Polarographic reduction of pertechnetate ion in 0.1 M potassium hydroxide[4]

Concn. (mM)	Wave A			Concn. (mM)	Wave B		
	i_d	n	$E_{1/2}$		i_d	n	$E_{1/2}$
0.130	1.24	2.25	− 0.85	0.130	0.56	1.00	− 1.14
0.130	1.20	2.20	− 0.85	0.130	0.56	1.00	− 1.14
0.108	1.04	2.05	− 0.86	0.108	0.56	1.20	− 1.16
0.108	0.96	2.03	− 0.86	0.108	0.56	1.20	− 1.16
0.087	0.72	1.95	− 0.85	0.087	0.36	0.95	− 1.16
0.087	0.76	2.05	− 0.85	0.087	0.36	0.95	− 1.16

Perrhenate and pertechnetate ions in potassium cyanide.—0.1 M potassium cyanide was found to be a very poor supporting electrolyte for the polarography of the perrhenate ion.[9] A large wave was obtained which seemed to consist of two components, but these were so poorly defined that no accurate measurements could be made upon them, although they appeared to represent a two- and a four-electron reduction respectively. This would be in agreement with the fact that cyanide stabilizes both Re^V and Re^I, and the polarographic behaviour of potassium octacyanorhenate(v) and potassium dioxotetracyanorhenate(v) described below agrees with this interpretation.

Potassium pertechnetate ion 0.1 M potassium cyanide gave only a single well defined wave with a half-wave potential of − 0.81 v corresponding to a three-electron reduction to Tc^{IV}.[4] The wave was irreversible. Technetium is in such a position in the periodic table that it would be difficult to predict whether it would form an octacyanide like molybdenum, tungsten or rhenium or a hexacyanide like chromium, manganese and ruthenium. If an octacyanide were formed the technetium must be at least in the + 5 state since there are too many electrons in lower valent technetium to allow the formation of d^4sp^3 hybrid bonds. However, if a hexacyanide were formed the technetium would probably be in the + 4 state. The polarographic evidence suggests that a cyanide of Tc^{IV} will be formed and it is noteworthy that so far no cyanide of Tc^V corresponding to the Re^V cyanides has been prepared.

Reduction of Other Rhenium Compounds

Potassium dioxotetracyanorhenate(v) and octacyanorhenate(v) in potassium cyanide and chloride solution.—Jezowska-Trzebiatowska[5] has investigated the polarographic reduction of potassium dioxotetracyanorhenate(v), $K_3[ReO_2(CN)_4]$, which in solution probably exists as $K_3[Re(OH)_4(CN)_4]$.

The diffusion coefficient of the anion was measured and found to be 0.7×10^{-5} cm²/sec. It was also found that in potassium cyanide this compound was reduced in one stage to Re^I and in potassium chloride to Re^{-I}.

Potassium octacyanorhenate was also reduced in these two supporting electrolytes.[4] In potassium cyanide a good wave was obtained with a half-wave potential of -1.75 v. In potassium chloride another good wave was obtained with a half-wave potential of -1.5 v. The results are shown in Table 9-3.

Table 9-3. Polarographic reduction of potassium octacyanorhenate(v) in potassium cyanide and chloride[4]

0.1 M potassium cyanide	Concn. (mM)	1.8		0.9	0.54	0.27		
	i_d (μA)	20.25	21.0	10.2	6.05	3.1		
	$i_d/\text{cm}^{2/3}\,t^{1/6}$	5.09	5.27	5.14	5.09	5.23		Mean 5.16
	$E_{1/2}$ (v)	-1.80		-1.76	-1.74	-1.72		
2 M potassium chloride	Concn. (mM)	1.8	0.0		0.54	0.378		
	i_d (μA)	31.5	15.3	15.5	9.6	6.4	6.2	
	$i_d/\text{cm}^{2/3}\,t^{1/6}$	7.95	7.73	7.82	7.77	7.77	7.73	Mean 7.79
	$E_{1/2}$ (v)	-1.45	-1.50		-1.52	-1.52	-1.52	

In order to calculate the n values it is necessary to make some assumption of the diffusion coefficient or to use some additional information. The ratio of the n values for potassium octacyanorhenate(v) in the two supporting electrolytes studied is the same as the ratio of the $i_d/\text{cm}^{2/3}t^{1/6}$ values, i.e. $5.16/7.79 = 2{:}3$ or $4{:}6$. In view of Jezowska's results for the similar dioxotetracyanorhenate(v) ion it is likely that the ratio is $4{:}6$, that is in potassium cyanide, potassium octacyanorhenate(v) is reduced to Re^I and in potassium chloride it is reduced to Re^{-I}.

The Rhenide State

Potassium perrhenate in potassium chloride solution.—The polarographic reduction of potassium perrhenate in potassium chloride solutions was first studied by Lundell and Knowles[6] who found an apparent n value of eight, that is reduction of Re^{VII} to Re^{-I}.

Lingane[1] made a comprehensive study of the reduction and studied the effect of perrhenate ion concentration. It was found that at the smallest perrhenate ion concentration (0.0192 mM) in 2 M potassium chloride a well defined wave was obtained with a half-wave potential of -1.41 v. As the perrhenate ion concentration was increased a second wave appeared at -1.7 v and a maximum formed on the first wave.

The height of the first wave was not strictly proportional to the perrhenate ion concentration even after correction for the residual current due to the supporting electrolyte and the apparent n value increased with decreasing perrhenate ion concentration, tending to a value of eight at the highest concentration studied (0.4 mM). Lingane concluded that the first wave at -1.41 v is due to the reduction of perrhenate ion to Re^{-I}. In unbuffered solution the reaction was thought to be

$$ReO_4^- + 4 H_2O + 8 e \rightarrow Re^{-1} + 8 OH^-$$

The small slope of the wave suggested that the reaction was irreversible. The second wave at -1.7 v was much larger than corresponds to reduction of Re^{VII}, and since its character was found to change markedly with the addition of gelatin, Lingane concluded that it was a catalytic wave.

In a more recent study on the polarographic reduction of perrhenate ion in 2 M potassium chloride these results of Lingane's have been fully confirmed and extended.[4] The reduction was studied over a wider concentration range of perrhenate ion and it was found that when this concentration exceeded 0.4 mM the n value is truly eight, but below this concentration it rises rapidly with decreasing concentration. The results of both Lingane and Colton *et al* are shown in Fig. 3.

It was also confirmed[4] that the half-wave potential varied with the perrhenate ion concentration as Lingane had found, but the later workers obtained values about 0.15 v more negative than those found by Lingane. Some experimental results obtained by Colton and coworkers are shown in Table 9-4.

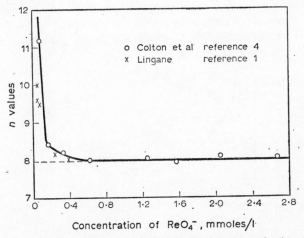

Concentration of ReO_4^-, mmoles/l

Figure 3. Variation of n values obtained in the polarographic reduction of potassium perrhenate at different concentrations in potassium chloride solutions (Reproduced from Colton *et al, J. Chem. Soc.* 71 (1960))

Table 9-4. Polarographic reduction of perrhenate ion in 2 M potassium chloride

Concn. (mM)	2.67	2.05	1.57	1.25	0.62	0.32	0.16	0.08
i_d (μA)	105	80.8	58.5	48.6	24.0	12.7	6.5	4.3
$i_d/cm^{2/3}/t^{1/6}$	17.7	17.8	17.2	17.7	17.6	18.0	18.6	24.4
n	8.04	8.09	7.90	8.04	8.0	8.20	8.40	11.20
$E_{1/2}$ (v)	− 1.61	− 1.57	− 1.56	− 1.56	− 1.55	− 1.55	− 1.55	− 1.55

Potassium pertechnetate in potassium chloride.—The polarographic reduction of potassium pertechnetate in 2 M potassium chloride has been found to be similar to that of potassium perrhenate.[4] However, more dilute solutions must be used to observe the reduction wave since above 0.1 mM the wave is distorted by a large maximum and this remains to a certain extent at all the concentrations studied. In very dilute solutions the n values increase with decreasing pertechnetate ion concentration as they do for rhenium. This effect is shown in Fig. 4.

In order to calculate n values from the Ilkovic equation the value of the diffusion coefficient for the pertechnetate ion was assumed to be the same as that for the perrhenate ion.[4] This was thought to be justified since it was known that the pertechnetate and perrhenate ions are of almost the same size and any small error in the diffusion coefficient would only have a small effect on n as only the square root of the diffusion coefficient is used in the Ilkovic equation. The assumed value of $D = 1.37 \times 10^{-5}/cm^2/sec$ gives a steady n value of 8.54. The deviation from 8.0 was thought to be due to difficulties in measuring the diffusion current accurately due to the maximum in the wave. This inherent inaccuracy is also reflected in the larger scatter of points in the constant region than is observed in the case of rhenium. It was found that the wave was irreversible. Some typical experimental results are given in Table 9-5.

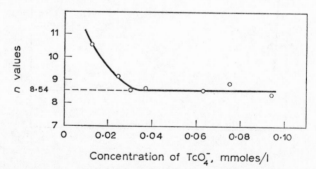

Figure 4. Variation of n values obtained in the polarographic reduction of potassium pertechnetate at different concentrations in potassium chloride solutions
(Reproduced from Colton *et al, J. Chem. Soc.* 71 (1960).)

Table 9-5. Polarographic reduction of potassium pertechnetate in potassium chloride

Concn. (mM)	0.094	0.075	0.063	0.037	0.030	0.024	0.012
i_d (μA)	3.8	3.2	2.6	1.55	1.24	0.96	0.60
$i_d/cm^{2/3}/t^{1/6}$	18.3	19.4	18.7	19.0	18.8	20	23
n	8.3	8.8	8.5	8.6	8.5	9.09	10.5
$E_{1/2}$ (v)	− 1.15	− 1.145	− 1.140	− 1.14	− 1.13	− 1.12	− 1.12

It is noteworthy that in a non-complexing medium the pertechnetate ion is reduced at a potential about 0.4 v less negative than that required to reduce perrhenate, indicating that Tc^{VII} is more easily reduced than Re^{VII} as might be expected.

Oxidation of the rhenide ion.—The polarographic (anodic) oxidation of the rhenide ion has been studied by Lingane[7] and by Rulfs and Elving[8] who obtained similar experimental results but differed in their interpretation.

Lingane prepared his rhenide solutions by passing a dilute solution of potassium perrhenate in dilute sulphuric or perchloric acid through a zinc amalgam reductor in a nitrogen atmosphere. Lundell and Knowles had previously shown that for a successful preparation of the rhenide state it was essential to exclude oxygen. In order to establish that the rhenium was in the −1 state, samples were titrated with ceric sulphate solution. It was found that oxidation was fairly slow so excess ceric solution was added, the mixture then allowed to stand for 15 minutes and the excess of cerium was then back titrated. It was found that on average one equivalent of rhenium required 7.9 equivalents of ceric sulphate for complete oxidation.

Lingane found that a typical polarogram of reduced rhenium in solution in dilute sulphuric acid showed three distinct anodic waves with half wave potentials of − 0.54; − 0.30 and − 0.05 v (*vs* s.c.e.) which he termed the α, β and γ waves respectively. A polarogram of the rhenide ion in dilute perchloric acid was similar except that the β wave was split into two components β' and β''. The sum of β' and β'' was equal to the height of β wave in dilute sulphuric acid.

Lingane assumed that the waves correspond to oxidation of Re^{-1} to successively higher oxidation states. The diffusion coefficient of the rhenide ion is unknown but from the ratio of the i_d/c values (i.e. the ratios of the n values) the following oxidation scheme was deduced.

$$\alpha \text{ wave} \quad Re^{-1} \text{ to } Re^{II}$$
$$\beta' \text{ wave} \quad Re^{-1} \text{ to } Re^{III}$$
$$\beta'' \text{ wave} \quad Re^{-1} \text{ to } Re^{V}$$
$$\gamma \text{ wave} \quad Re^{-1} \text{ to } Re^{VII}$$

Lundell and Knowles[8] had shown that a solution of Re^{-1} in dilute sulphuric acid which had been warmed to $50°$ turned brown and required six equivalents of oxidant for complete oxidation. Lingane was able to show polarographically that this solution was not Re^I but a mixture of Re^{-1} and higher oxidation states.

Rulfs and Elving[8] obtained similar waves to those of Lingane but they postulate a different oxidation scheme. Five waves were found in dilute sulphuric acid and their assignments were as follows.

wave A	Re^{-1} to Re^I	$E_{1/2} = -0.505$ v
wave A'		$E_{1/2} = -0.38$ v
wave B	Re^I to Re^{II}	$E_{1/2} = -0.268$ v
wave C	Re^{II} to Re^{III}	$E_{1/2} = -0.020$ v
wave D	probably oxidation of Re^{III}	$E_{1/2} = +0.17$ v

The A wave exhibited only a moderate shift with temperature and acidity and no shift with rhenide concentration in accord with the expected behaviour of a reversible wave and gave $n = 2$. The half-wave potential was thought to be the true potential of the Re^{-1}/Re^{+1} couple. Wave A' and D were too small to be read with precision. Waves B and C were probably irreversible but gave n values of one.

Rulfs and Elving carried out further experiments to support their reaction scheme. The polarograms of a rhenide solution were recorded after addition of each successive equivalent of potassium dichromate until eight equivalents had been added. It appeared that some of the lower oxidation states persist through several stages and they agree with Lingane's suggestion that solutions obtained by warming rhenide solutions in dilute sulphuric acid are not really Re^I but mixtures. Rulfs and Elving found that the B wave persists only so long as the A wave is present, and this is interpreted as showing that Re^I has little tendency for independent existence in dilute sulphuric acid.

They also found that potassium hexachlororhenate(IV), K_2ReCl_6, in dilute sulphuric acid gave no anodic wave before $+0.2$ v where the calomel discharge occurs. To show that this was not due solely to complexing they also used reactive Re^{IV} species formed by dissolving freshly precipitated rhenium dioxide in dilute hydrochloric acid and diluting with sulphuric acid, all in the absence of oxygen. These easily oxidized species showed no oxidation waves either and Rulfs and Elving take this to mean that the pattern observed for Re^{-1} oxidation must involve oxidation of Re^{-1} only to Re^{III} or less.

The potential of the Re^{-1}/Re^I couple was approximately confirmed by chemical tests. 0.5 mM Re^{-1} solution in 2 N sulphuric acid was mixed with dilute solutions of oxidized forms of various compounds. It was found to reduce Cu(I) but not Co(II), so that the potential of the Re^{-1}/Re^{I} couple should lie between + 0.28 and 0.19 v vs n.h.e. This agrees quite well with the polarographic half-wave potential of − 0.505 v vs s.c.e. or + 0.26 v vs n.h.e.

Some interesting observations were made by Rulfs and Elving on the comparative stability of rhenide solutions in various media. They found that in dilute sulphuric acid quantitative reduction of Re^{VII} to Re^{-1} occurred only if the rhenium concentration was less than 0.83 mM. In dilute hydrochloric acid quantitative reduction was possible up to 1.3 mM and if pyridinium chloride was added to the hydrochloric acid solution 2.6 mM rhenide could be produced quantitatively. They also found definite evidence that solutions in the two acids were different, those in dilute sulphuric turned brown and produced a precipitate on exposure to air, but those in hydrochloric acid turned clear yellow and gave no precipitate.

There is also polarographic evidence[9] that pyridine, thiocyanate and ethylenediamine all complex with Re^{-1} to give complexes that could not be oxidized at − 0.1 v. It is also known that cyanide complexes[4, 5] and phosphine complexes[9] of rhenium can be reduced polarographically to Re^{-1} and it may be that in time many complexes of Re^{-1} will be isolated.

Independent observations on the chemical reactions of the rhenide ion strongly support the interpretation of the polarographic results suggested by Rulfs and Elving. Maun and Davidson[10] prepared their rhenide solution in the usual way using hydrochloric acid solutions and reducing with zinc. They found it impossible to quantitatively reduce Re^{VII} to Re^{-1} in concentrations greater than 1 mM. The solutions were colourless but became brownish on standing in air. They found that the most characteristic test for the rhenide ion was the production of metallic copper when the solution, in less than 0.5 M hydrochloric acid was titrated with cupric sulphate solution. The solutions also gave a heavy black precipitate with mercuric nitrate and decolourized potassium permanganate solution. The reduced solutions developed little colour on standing in the absence of air. Mixtures of Re^{VII} and Re^{-1} developed a brown colour which was attributed to Re^{I} and Re^{IV}, but irrespective of the validity of these oxidation state assignments, the fact that Re^{-1} solutions are colourless even after standing shows that they contain no Re^{VII} or any of the highly coloured intermediate oxidation states.

Maun and Davidson[10] presented evidence which strongly suggests that Re^{-1} in 4 M hydrochloric acid is oxidized by oxygen, Cu^{II} and Re^{VII} to yellow brown solutions of Re^{I} and that this may be further oxidized to Re^{IV} by oxygen or Re^{VII}.

When a solution of Re^{-1} was exposed to air its visible absorption spectrum studied, three well defined stages were observed. After 3 hours exposure a yellow-brown substance had formed ($\lambda_{max} = 610$ mμ). After 15 hours' formation of a yellow-green product occurred ($\lambda_{max} = 690$ mμ) and the peak at 610 mμ decreased. After 40 hours the peak at 690 mμ decreased.

When oxygen was bubbled through Re^{-1} solutions they went brown rapidly. After 5 minutes the change in the reduction titre of the solutions corresponded to a change from Re^{-1} to Re^{+1}. Further oxidation was slower. This strongly suggested that the peak at 610 mμ was due to Re^{+1}.

Similar changes were observed when perrhenate ion was added to rhenide solutions in 4 M hydrochloric acid. Solutions with average oxidation number of + 1 gave a peak at 610 mμ. This developed fully in 10–40 minutes and did not alter over 40 hours. Addition of excess perrhenate caused a decrease in the peak at 610 mμ and a new peak formed at 690 mμ.

Re^{-1} in dilute hydrochloric acid solution is also oxidized by Cu^{II}. The first addition of copper sulphate gave a black precipitate of metallic copper and a brown solution which did not contain copper. Further addition of copper sulphate decolourized the solution and produced Cu^{I}. On the basis of semi quantitative results Maun and Davidson suggested the following oxidation schemes.

$$Re^{-1} + O_2 \rightarrow Re^{I}$$
$$3\,Re^{-1} + Re^{VII} \rightarrow 4\,Re^{I}$$
$$Re^{I} + Re^{VII} \rightarrow 2\,Re^{IV}$$
$$Re^{-1} + Cu^{II} \rightarrow Re^{I} + Cu$$
$$Re^{I} + Cu^{II} \rightarrow Re^{>I} + Cu^{I}$$

The structure of the rhenide ion.—The first coherent ideas about the structure of the rhenide ion were suggested by Pauling[11] who pointed out out that Re^{-1} is iso-electronic with Pt^{II}. He suggested that the rhenide ion consisted of a rhenium atom in the $-$ 1 oxidation state coordinated to four molecules of water at the corners of a square planar arrangement.

Since 1954 several papers have appeared concerning the isolation of solid *rhenides*, various formulae have been assigned to these compounds and it is by no means certain which, if any, of them is the rhenide produced by reduction of potassium perrhenate in acid solutions. For convenience however, all these compounds will be referred to as *rhenides*.

Isolation of Solid Rhenides

Bravo, Griswold and Kleinberg[12] isolated the first solid rhenide by reducing potassium perrhenate with potassium metal in a water–ethylenediamine mixture in a nitrogen atmosphere. The white solid which resulted from the reaction was potassium rhenide together with potassium hydroxide. By repeated extractions of potassium hydroxide with isopropyl alcohol a progressively darker solid was produced. Bravo *et al* admit that there was always a little unreduced potassium perrhenate in the reaction product but they claimed this could be separated. Pure potassium rhenide was never obtained, the product was always contaminated with potassium hydroxide, the amount of hydroxide was estimated by determining the potassium content and assuming the excess over that required for $KRe(H_2O)_4$ was due to potassium hydroxide. It appears that the formula $KRe(H_2O)_4$ was accepted without any evidence except Pauling's proposal. In the light of later results the whole analytical procedure is extremely dubious as later workers found significant amounts of potassium perrhenate and potassium carbonate in their products. Nevertheless it is clear that Bravo *et al* did form a rhenide since they observed that addition of thallous nitrate to the rhenide solution gave a precipitate which rapidly decomposed. The precipitation of thallous rhenide has become accepted as a test of the presence of rhenide ion. All later attempts to prepare rhenides followed the same general method used by Bravo *et al.*

Floss and Grosse[13] used lithium reduction of perrhenate in aqueous solution and separated the bulk of the lithium hydroxide by precipitation as the phosphate. The solution of lithium rhenide was purified by ion exchange on a cation exchanger in the ammonium form. Addition of various bases gave different salts of the rhenides. Evidence was presented that salts such as $Ba[Re(H_2O)_4]_2$ were formed. The salts were colourless, crystalline, thermally stable salts. They were found to be stable in alkali solution but they decomposed in solution below pH 7. The solids were slowly oxidized by oxygen.

It was shown at this stage that the substance formed by reduction of potassium perrhenate with potassium in aqueous ethylenediamine solution was in fact a rhenium hydride.[14, 15] The nuclear magnetic resonance spectrum of the solution showed a peak at 15 p.p.m. on the high field side in a region where transition metal hydrides are known to give resonances.

Ginsberg *et al*[15] isolated the rhenide as described by Bravo *et al.* The grey-brown solid was purified by dissolving in an alkaline methanol–water mixture (5:1), centrifuging off the brown insoluble material and precipitating the rhenide by pouring the clear supernatant liquid into oxygen free anhydrous isopropanol. The solid rhenide was stable in an inert atmosphere.

In a second paper Floss and Grosse[16] abandoned their lithium reduction method and reverted to the potassium reduction procedure. After extracting the bulk of the potassium hydroxide the solution was fed into a cooled column of cation exchanger in the ammonia form. The eluent was checked for appearance of the rhenide with thallous hydroxide and for potassium by the flame test. Only the fraction free from potassium was collected. The amount of rhenide was determined analytically and the stoichiometric amounts of potassium or barium hydroxides were added, after which the salts were obtained by evaporation at 0°. The yield of the potassium salt was about 77%. Samples were thought to be free of perrhenate since they gave no precipitate with tetraphenylarsonium chloride solution. The oxidation equivalent with potassium permanganate was shown to be 7.9 ± 0.2.

The thermal decomposition of the potassium and barium rhenohydrides was studied quantitatively. Decomposition began above 250° and was complete at 450°. After the hydrogen evolution had ceased, the water formed was frozen out and weighed. The volume of hydrogen was measured and the potassium and rhenium determined. The results were

$$K : Re(std) : H : O \text{ (as KOH)} = 1.1 : 1 : 4.1 : 1.96;$$

that is the compound is $KReH_4 \cdot 2H_2O$

The equations for the thermal decomposition of the salts were found to be

$$KReH_4 \cdot 2H_2O \quad \rightarrow Re + \tfrac{5}{2}H_2 + KOH + H_2O$$

$$Ba(ReH_4)_2 \cdot 4H_2O \rightarrow 2\,Re + 5\,H_2 + BaO + 3\,H_2O$$

More recently Ginsberg, Miller and Koubek[17] have revised their earlier ideas on the rhenohydride and they now formulate it as potassium octahydridorhenate(VI), K_2ReH_8. The material was produced in the usual way from potassium perrhenate in aqueous ethylenediamine reduced by potassium metal. The bulk of the potassium hydroxide was removed by isopropanol extractions when a brown product remained. This was dissolved in potassium hydroxide solution, centrifuged and the colourless supernatant was poured into 97–98% ethylenediamine to give a white precipitate of potassium octahydridorhenate(VI) contaminated with potassium carbonate, potassium perrhenate and water. The product was repeatedly extracted with 97–98% ethylenediamine until the infra-red spectrum showed no bands due to carbonate or perrhenate. The product was finally dissolved in potassium hydroxide, precipitated by isopropanol and after extraction by isopropanol dried in nitrogen. The yield was about 16%. The material was analysed for potassium and rhenium.

The oxidation of the material in alkaline solution was investigated by adding weighed amounts of the hydride to known volumes of calcium hypochlorite in a closed system. The hydrogen evolution was measured and excess hypochlorite determined by titration. Acid decomposition of the material was also studied.

From these results the formula K_2ReH_8 was deduced. In acid solution it was found that $H_{evolved}/Re = 10$

$$ReH_8{}^{2-} + 2H^+ = Re^0 + 5H_2$$

and the hypochlorite oxidation gave

$$ReH_8{}^{2-} + 6ClO^- = ReO_4{}^- + \tfrac{5}{2}H_2 + OH^- + H_2O + 6Cl^-$$

for which $H_{evolved}/Re = 5$

The ratio $ReH = 1:8$ was confirmed by n.m.r. measurements. The peak height due to the hydride in D_2O and 45% KOD was first measured and then compared to the peak height of known amounts of water in deuterium oxide.

The infra-red spectrum of both pure and impure K_2ReH_8 were given; the impurities were shown to be potassium perrhenate and potassium carbonate and the spectrum of the impure material is very similar to that given by Floss and Grosse for allegedly pure $ReH_4{}^-$.[16]

Recently single crystals of K_2ReH_8 have been obtained and they have been studied by x-ray diffraction techniques.[18] The lattice constants of K_2ReH_8 are $a = 9.61$ and $c = 5.51$ Å. The observed density was 3.07 ± 0.1 and for three formula units per unit cell the theoretical density is 3.09 g/cc.

The gross features only allowed rhenium to be fixed in the positions 1(a), 000 and 2(d), $\pm \tfrac{1}{3}, \tfrac{2}{3}, \tfrac{1}{2}$ of space group $D_{6h}{}'-P\,6/mmn$. Absorption errors were largely due to the size of the crystals and the positions of potassium atoms were not fixed.

The rhenium atoms are widely spaced in the lattice, the smallest Re–Re distance is 5.51 Å so discrete $ReH_8{}^{2-}$ ions were thought to exist.

A recent neutron diffraction study of the rhenide[19] has revealed that the compound is in fact potassium enneahydridorhenate(VII), K_2ReH_9. Each rhenium atom is surrounded by a trigonal prism of hydrogen atoms with three additional hydrogen atoms beyond the centres of the prism faces. The average Re–H distance is 1.68 ± 0.01Å. The fact that the rhenide is now thought to be a compound of Re(VII) removes the previous difficulty of it being diamagnetic.

There is no evidence whatsoever that the *rhenides* isolated by alkali reduction of potassium perrhenate are the same as the compound formed by polarographic reduction of perrhenate or by acid reduction, in a Jones reduction, of potassium perrhenate. Indeed Ginsberg and Koubek[20] have investigated this point and they arrived at the conclusion that the materials are different, based on the following observations:

(a) Polarographic results[4] show that in 2 M potassium chloride $ReO_4{}^-$ to rhenide gives $n = 8$. Also polarographic oxidation of rhenide also gives $n = 8$. Thus if the rhenide is a hydride it must be such that oxidation oʃ H^+ and rhenium to perrhenate corresponds to $n = 8$ and this is not the case for ReH_4^- or ReH_8^{2-}.

(b) The rhenide solutions formed in alkali media do not give a stable precipitate with thallous nitrate, as mentioned earlier the precipitation of the thallous salt has become diagnostic of the presence of the original rhenide prepared in acid solution.

It could not be shown whether the material is a hydride or not because of the low limiting concentration of rhenide in acid solution.[1]

References

1. J. J. LINGANE, *J. Am. Chem. Soc.* **64**, 1001 (1942.)
2. C. J. RULFS and P. J. ELVING, *J. Am. Chem. Soc.* **73**, 3284 (1951).
3. See for example I. M. KOLTHOFF and J. J. LINGANE, *Polarography* Interscience, New York (1952).
4. R. COLTON, J. DALZIEL, W. P. GRIFFITH and G. WILKINSON, *J. Chem. Soc.* 71 (1960).
5. B. JEZOWSKA-TRZEBIATOWSKA, *Chem. Tech. Berlin* **9**, 470 (1957).
6. G. E. F. LUNDELL and H. B. KNOWLES, *J. Res. Nat. Bur. Std. A* **18**, 629 (1937).
7. J. J. LINGANE, *J. Am. Chem. Soc.* **64**, 2182 (1942).
8. C. J. RULFS and P. J. ELVING, *J. Am. Chem. Soc.* **73**, 3287 (1951).
9. R. COLTON, R. LEVITUS and G. WILKINSON, *J. Chem. Soc.* 4121 (1960).
10. E. K. MAUN and N. DAVIDSON, *J. Am. Chem. Soc.* **72**, 3509 (1950).
11. L. PAULING, *Chem. Eng. News* **25**, 2970 (1947).
12. J. B. BRAVO, E. GRISWOLD and J. KLEINBERG, *J. Phys. Chem.* **58**, 18 (1954).
13. J. G. FLOSS and A. V. GROSSE, *J. Inorg. Nucl. Chem.* **9**, 318 (1959).
14. R. COLTON, J. DALZIEL, W. P. GRIFFITH and G. WILKINSON, *Nature* **183**, 1755 (1959).
15. A. P. GINSBERG, J. M. MILLER, J. R. CAVANAUGH and B. P. DAILEY, *Nature* **185** 528 (1960).
16. J. G. FLOSS and A. V. GROSSE, *J. Inorg. Nucl. Chem.* **16**, 36 (1960).
17. A. P. GINSBERG, J. M. MILLER and E. KOUBEK, *J. Am. Chem. Soc.* **83**, 4909 (1961).
18. K. KNOX and A. P. GINSBERG, *Inorg. Chem.* **1**, 945 (1962).
19. S. C. ABRAHAMS, A. P. GINSBERG and K. KNOX, *Inorg. Chem.* **3**, 558 (1964).
20. A. P. GINSBERG and E. KOUBEK, *Z. Anorg. Allgem. Chem.* **315**, 278 (1962).

10

Miscellaneous Topics

Reduction of Perrhenate Ion

The reduction of perrhenate ion by a variety of reducing agents has been studied in a number of solvents, both complexing and non-complexing. These reactions have been followed analytically by estimating the oxidation state to which the rhenium has been reduced, and also spectrophotometrically. In most of the experiments discussed in this section no compounds have actually been isolated and this is a major reason why the results have been treated separately from similar reactions in which the reduction products have been isolated. Nevertheless studies on these solution reactions have shown that a large number of complex compounds exist in intermediate oxidation states of rhenium.

The simplest case of all is the electrolytic reduction of perrhenate ion in a non-complexing medium.[1] In 6.0 M perchloric acid, using a platinum cathode, the net reaction was reduction of perchlorate ion to chloride. This was shown by the fact that the intensity of the perrhenate absorption bands were unaltered after three faradays of electricity had passed through the solution. In addition the solution gave a strong positive test for chloride ion. In the less easily reduced trifluoroacetic and ethanesulphonic acids reduction of perrhenate led to the formation of insoluble oxide, probably rhenium dioxide.[1]

Several workers have investigated the reduction of perrhenate ion in hydrochloric acid solutions. There is no doubt that the final product is the hexachlororhenate(IV) ion but there are a number of observable intermediate stages. Electrolytic reduction of potassium perrhenate in 6 M or 8 M hydrochloric acid using a platinized gauze gave reduction to Re^V in the presence of potassium iodide or hydriodic acid. A compound was isolated which was originally[2] given the formula $K_2[Re(OH)_2Cl_5]$, but this was modified in a later paper[3] to the much more likely formula $K_2[ReOCl_5]$.

The electrolytic reduction is undoubtedly complicated and it was suggested that it consisted of three stages[3]

$$ReO_4^- + HCl \rightarrow ReO_2Cl_4^- + 2\,H_2O$$
$$ReO_2Cl_4^- \rightarrow ReO_2Cl_4^{2-} \rightarrow ReO_2Cl_4^{3-}$$
$$ReO_2Cl_4^{3-} + H^+ + HCl \rightarrow ReOCl_5^{2-} + H_2O$$

No further evidence to support the formulation of these intermediate stages has been reported.

The reduction of a cold solution of potassium perrhenate in hydrochloric acid by hydriodic acid was also studied[3] and was shown to occur in two stages

$$Re^{VII} + 2\,I^- \rightarrow Re^V + 2\,I$$
$$Re^V + I^- \rightarrow Re^{IV} + I$$

By the addition of potassium or ammonium chloride the yellowish green salts $(K, NH_4)_2ReOCl_5$ were isolated.

Maun and Davidson[4] studied the reduction of perrhenate ion by stannous chloride in hydrochloric acid solutions. By adding varying amounts of stannous chloride to the perrhenate solution in 4 M acid and examining the solutions spectrophotometrically they were able to show that rapid reduction occurred to Re^V followed by slow reduction to Re^{IV}. By adding exactly two equivalents of stannous chloride solutions containing only Re^V were obtained. The oxidation state of the rhenium was checked by titration against ceric salts. The light-green Re^V solution was stable in solution and was unaffected by oxygen. Attempts to prepare the Re^V species in approximately 2 M or 3 M hydrochloric acid led to disproportionation to Re^{IV} and Re^{VII}.

Addition of three equivalents of stannous chloride to potassium perrhenate in 4 M hydrochloric acid gave a strongly coloured yellow brown solution which contained Re^{IV}. By varying the amount of stannous chloride added it was shown that a single well-defined species was formed.[4] The absorption remained constant over a period of days. The yellow-brown species was stable towards oxygen, but chlorine and ceric sulphate oxidized the rhenium to perrhenate.

Yet another Re^{IV} solution was prepared by the dissolution of rhenium dioxide in 12 M hydrochloric acid at room temperature, but examination of the absorption spectra of several solutions prepared in the same way showed that the substance was not a well-defined species, rather a mixture.

Potassium hexachlororhenate(IV) in hydrochloric acid was found to be very resistant towards oxidation by ceric sulphate. Maun and Davidson[4] suggested that the yellow brown species contained some rhenium–oxygen bonds, either a series of hydroxo ions of the type $ReCl_{6-n}(OH)_n{}^{2-}$ or a series of polymers with rhenium–oxygen–rhenium bonds. It should be possible to distinguish between these alternatives by measuring the magnetic moment of the species in solution by the n.m.r. method.[5] The monomeric species would be paramagnetic but an oxygen-bridged polymer would probably be diamagnetic.

Other solutions said to contain Re^{IV} and Re^{V} have been prepared by the electrolytic reduction of perrhenic acid in hydrochloric acid solutions.[1] Reduction of approximately 0.09 M perrhenic acid in 4 M hydrochloric acid at a mercury cathode gave an olive green solution which corresponded to an oxidation state of 4.06 ± 0.06. This was obviously a mixture of complexes since the spectra of several samples were only qualitatively similar. No species resembling the reactive yellow-brown species reported by Maun and Davidson[4] were observed.

Reduction of perrhenic acid in 8 M hydrochloric acid at a platinum electrode gave a clear light green solution with an average oxidation state of 4.96 ± 0.03. As initially prepared, Re^{V} solutions all contained a small amount of a species which absorbed at 4010 Å, but on standing this disappeared and a yellow green equilibrium mixture was obtained. This was characterized by bands at 4800 and 4160 Å. The equilibrium solution of Re^{V} was only very slowly oxidized by air. By varying the concentration of hydrochloric acid the two major peaks in the Re^{V} solution decreased at different rates which very strongly suggested that a mixture was present in solution.[1]

Rhenium complexes which are prepared by the reduction of Re^{VII} in sulphuric acid solutions have also been investigated. Holeman[6] investigated the effect of various reducing agents upon potassium perrhenate in varying concentrations of sulphuric acid. Ferrous sulphate, stannous sulphate and titanous sulphate all reduced Re^{VII} to Re^{V}, the course of the reaction was followed potentiometrically. However, chromous sulphate caused reduction to Re^{IV}. There was no indication of Re^{VI} except at low temperatures and very high sulphuric acid concentrations.

In a much more recent investigation Busey and Larson[7] investigated the reduction of potassium perrhenate by stannous sulphate, in 18 M sulphuric acid solution. The course of the reaction was followed spectrophotometrically. The absorption of the Re^{VI} species did not obey Beer's Law and in addition the deviation was not the same over the whole spectrum suggesting that more than one species was present. Curves of the optical density at selected wavelengths of the number of equivalents of stannous sulphate added per mole of perrhenate did not show a sharp change at a ratio of unity which was taken to indicate a disproportion of Re^{VI} to Re^{VII}

M

and Re^V. Dilution curves of the Re^{VI} solution were interpreted on the basis that the principle Re^{VI} species was a dimer in equilibrium with a monomer. Addition of two equivalents of stannous sulphate gave Re^V which could not be further reduced by stannous salts in this medium agreeing with the observations of Holeman.[6]

The electrolytic reduction of perrhenate ion in sulphuric acid solutions has been investigated.[8] Depending on the acid concentration and potential used, perrhenate was cathodically reduced to Re^V or Re^{IV}. These lower states were not obtained as true solutions but rather as suspensions. The action of oxygen on Re^{IV} and Re^V suspensions in dilute sulphuric acid produced violet solutions that could be reduced to amber solutions. It was suggested that the amber solution contained Re^V and the violet solution contained a mixed Re^V–Re^{VI} species.

The Catalytic Properties of Rhenium Compounds

The catalytic properties of rhenium metal and a few rhenium compounds have been studied but no extensive commercial use has so far been made of the results. By far most of the work has been concerned with the catalytic properties of the metal itself and several types of reaction have been studied.

Dehydrogenation reactions.—Dehydrogenation reactions were studied by Russian workers some years ago using rhenium catalysts prepared by the hydrogen reduction of ammonium perrhenate. They found that rhenium is a good catalyst for the dehydrogenation of butanol at 350–450° to give butaldehyde with almost no side reactions.[9] The energy of activation of the reaction was 12–13 kcal/mole at 400°. Isobutanol gave methylethylketone with greater difficulty under the same conditions.

A similarly prepared metal catalyst was used to study the dehydrogenation of propyl and isopropyl alcohols, comparisons being made with a copper catalyst.[10] It was found that the optimum temperature was about 400° and that in both cases, but particularly for isopropanol, rhenium was a better dehydrogenation catalyst than copper. With a rhenium catalyst at 400°, 20.8% propionaldehyde was obtained from propyl alcohol. The product was not decomposed, the amounts of carbon monoxide and hydrocarbons being negligible and the ratio of propionaldehyde to hydrogen being almost unity.[2] The dehydrogenation of isopropyl alcohol was much more rapid and the yield of acetone (85% at 400°) was considerably greater than that obtained using a copper catalyst; no solid or liquid byproducts were obtained. The energies of activation for the reactions were 30 kcal/mole (250–400°) for propyl alcohol and 14 kcal/mole for isopropyl alcohol.[10]

The dehydrogenation of cyclohexane and cyclohexene to give benzene has also been studied using a rhenium catalyst prepared either by reduction of ammonium perrhenate or by reduction of the dioxan–rhenium hepta-oxide complex.[11] It was found that the catalyst produced from ammonium perrhenate produced benzene from cyclohexane twice as rapidly as from cyclohexene. However the catalyst produced from the dioxan complex exhibited different behaviour producing benzene about twice as quickly from cyclohexene as from cyclohexane. It was also found that by preparing a series of catalysts as dispersed powders on a variety of carriers that the rate of dehydrogenation of cyclohexane was dependent to a significant extent on the nature of the carrier.[12]

Hydrogenation reactions.—Metallic rhenium is only a weak catalyst in hydrogenation reactions. Maleic acid in aqueous solution and cyclohexene in alcohol at 15–20 atm pressure were hardly reduced.[13] Rhenium from ammonium perrhenate supported on a ceramic surface was rather more reactive in catalysing the hydrogenation of cyclohexene, benzene and nitrobenzene at 200–400°.

Rhenium or rhenium–copper catalysts assist reactions such as the reduction of carbon monoxide to methane and ethylene to ethane. It was found incidentally that passing carbon monoxide over rhenium–copper catalysts at 470° produced rhenium carbide.[14]

Although rhenium is not a strong hydrogenating catalyst it can have an activating effect on a nickel catalyst.[15] Thus when rhenium was deposited on a nickel catalyst it was found to increase the hydrogenation of tetra-methylbutynediol and vinylactylenyldimethylcarbinol. The activating action depended on the amount of rhenium in the catalyst and for the carbinol 5% rhenium in the catalyst was the optimum amount.

Decomposition of ammonia.—Rhenium metal has been used as a catalyst to promote the decomposition of ammonia.[16] The kinetics of the reaction were studied between 380–440°, with and without added nitrogen, hydrogen and helium. They conform to those obtained using iron catalysts and show that the decomposition is proportional to $[NH_3]^{0.53}$ and $[H_2]^{-0.89}$ with nitrogen being inert. Chemisorption and decomposition of small amounts of ammonia were found to occur at low temperatures and pressures. The data indicated strong nitrogen adsorption, weak hydrogen adsorption and general surface homogeniety.

Decomposition of formic acid.—The catalytic activity of rhenium metal towards the decomposition of formic acid has been studied by Russian workers,[17] who found that formic acid was decomposed to carbon monoxide and water as follows

100°	8.7%	decomposition
150°	30.8%	decomposition
175°	57.6%	decomposition
230°	100%	decomposition
250°	100%	decomposition

M*

Catalytic properties of rhenium oxides.—Very soon after the discovery of rhenium it was found that the oxide dissolved in hydrochloric acid exhibited some catalytic properties especially in oxidation reactions such as sulphur dioxide to trioxide, sulphite to sulphate, nitrite to nitrate but no commercial applications seem to have been made of these properties.[18]

More recently the catalytic properties of *rhenium blacks* in hydrogenation reactions have been studied.[19] The *rhenium blacks* were prepared by hydrogenation of rhenium heptaoxide in an inert solvent *ex situ*, or in the presence of the substrate to be reduced *in situ*.

Ex situ catalysts were prepared in several solvents, the ease of reduction depended on the solvent, easiest in *p*-dioxan and water but difficult in ethanol. Generally speaking the catalytic activity of these catalysts was not exceptional but they did catalyse the hydrogenation of nitrobenzene to aniline, styrene to ethylbenzene. One noticeable feature was that ketones were reduced more easily than olefin groups which is opposite to the usual effect and advantage was taken of this property in the preparation of crotyl alcohol from crotonaldehyde (94% yield). For these *ex situ* catalysts analysis suggested that the catalyst was in fact rhenium metal.

In contrast, the catalyst in *in situ* reactions appeared to be a lower oxide of rhenium, possibly hydrated rhenium monoxide. The predominant property of these catalysts was the extraordinary ease of reduction of carboxylic acids to alcohols. This occurred at 150–170° for monocarboxylic acids, 200–250° for dicarboxylic acids under 135–270 atm of hydrogen. These temperatures are generally 100–250° lower than for other catalysts. In all cases there was virtually no unreacted acid. The reduction also proceeds for substituted acids without attack on other active centres, e.g. phenylacetic acid gives β-phenylethyl alcohol without affecting the aromatic ring, and crotonic acid gives propylene glycol.

Catalytic properties of rhenium sulphides.—Rhenium heptasulphide was prepared by the action of hydrogen sulphide on potassium perrhenate solution, and its catalytic activity in hydrogenation reactions was studied using ethanol as the solvent.[20] It was found that rhenium heptasulphide was remarkably resistant to catalytic poisoning. With this catalyst a conjugated carbon–carbon double bond such as in benzene or styrene, was much more easily reduced than an isolated double bond in cyclohexene.

Dimethylphenylcarbinol was easily dehydrated and reduced in one step. The ketone group in acetophenone was more difficult to reduce than the carbon–carbon double bond in styrene and the reduction of acetophenone to the carbinol was accompanied by considerable debenzylation particularly at high temperatures.

On the laboratory scale rhenium sulphide or rhenium metal catalysts have been shown to be effective catalysts for cracking brown coal tars to about 73 octane petrol at high hydrogen pressures.[21]

Rhenium disulphide catalyses the dehydration of methanol, ethanol and isopropanol to give good yields of the corresponding aldehydes and ketones with very small amounts of by-products at 400–500°.[22]

Finally, the catalytic activity of rhenium heptaselenide, prepared by the action of hydrogen selenide on potassium perrhenate solution, has been investigated. It was found that it was comparable in activity to rhenium heptasulphide, catalysing the hydrogenation of nitrobenzene to aniline. The catalyst was stable in air and poisoned only by arsenic.

No investigations of the use of technetium or its compounds as catalysts have been reported.

Corrosion Inhibition by Technetium

It has been found that the pertechnetate ion has a remarkable capacity to inhibit corrosion of mild steel. It was found that a certain minimum concentration of technetium is required to affect inhibition, but this concentration is low. A mild steel plate was exposed to aerated water at 250° and corrosion was completely inhibited by 5×10^{-5} M potassium pertechnetate.[24] The minimum concentration of technetium to give corrosion protection was usually in the range 5–50 p.p.m. In some inhibition experiments some β activity was always retained on the metal surfaces even after careful washing with water. The deposits on the cathode dissolved instantly in dilute hydrogen peroxide and were thought to be technetium dioxide, but brown films appeared on the anode also which did not dissolve in hydrogen peroxide easily and their nature remains obscure.[24]

The process of corrosion inhibition is not well understood but some general observations were made. It was found that the amount of technetium on the steel surface depended upon the state of the surface, whether it was scratched or polished. If a steel sample was first protected in a solution of potassium pertechnetate more concentrated than the limiting concentration and the solution then diluted, protection ceased. The association of a technetium deposit with anode processes suggested that this deposit was a secondary reaction effect but even an abundance of such a deposit did not inhibit corrosion in the absence of technetium solution.

In an effort to gain more knowledge of the inhibition process Cartledge[25] investigated the inhibition by potassium pertechnetate in the presence of both potassium perrhenate and sodium sulphate. The concentration of technetium was 3.6×10^{-4} M which was well above the limiting concentration for inhibition. Addition of 0.01 M potassium perrhenate or 0.005 M sodium sulphate interfered with the inhibition process. Mild steel exposed to the sulphate solution at 100° began rusting almost immediately but the specimen in the perrhenate solution remained bright for an hour. At 23° there were small areas of attack of samples in the perrhenate solution after 4 days, but similar samples in the sulphate solution were severely attacked. It is evident therefore that both perrhenate and sulphate interfere with the inhibiting effect of the pertechnetate ion although perrhenate is not so bad as sulphate.

Cartledge[25] also showed that perrhenate ion itself had no inhibiting effect on the corrosion of mild steel.

Recovery of Residues

Recovery of technetium from laboratory residues is usually essential, and for rhenium desirable, because of the cost of the elements. The author has employed several methods, the actual choice depending upon the impurities present in the residues and the form in which the purified product is required.

Rhenium in comparatively rich residues may readily be recovered by oxidizing all the rhenium to perrhenate using either hydrogen peroxide or nitric acid. The solution is then neutralized with potassium hydroxide and evaporated to a small volume and allowed to cool. Potassium perrhenate crystallizes and may be purified by recrystallization. This is an easy way to recover rhenium but unfortunately potassium perrhenate is not a very convenient starting material for the preparation of many rhenium compounds. Many halide preparations require the use of rhenium metal and potassium perrhenate is very difficult to reduce completely to the metal. Even if reduction is complete and all oxygen is removed, considerable amounts of potassium remain in the metal which may markedly effect the chemical behaviour of the metal, for example in chlorination. Thus, except in a few cases, potassium perrhenate is not a useful form in which to recover rhenium. This method is not readily applicable to technetium in any case, as potassium pertechnetate is far more soluble than potassium perrhenate.

Residues which only contain alkali metals and halide impurities with rhenium or technetium may readily be purified by evaporating with concentrated hydrochloric acid with a little hydriodic acid present. This treatment converts both metals to the MCl_6^{2-} ions. Addition of potassium chloride gives potassium hexachlororhenate (technate) (IV). This is a very useful form in which to recover the elements. The chlororhenate itself is a common starting material for preparations of rhenium compounds, it may also be readily converted to the corresponding bromo- and iodo-rhenates by treatment with the appropriate halogen acid. Hydrolysis by alkali solution gives rhenium dioxide which again is a useful starting point itself and it may also be readily converted to rhenium heptaoxide or reduced to rhenium metal. These reactions apply equally well to technetium.

Other recovery procedures of less general application have also been used. In their studies of technetium carbonyl compounds Hileman and coworkers[27] oxidized their residues to pertechnetate which was then reduced by acetaldehyde in alkali solution to the dioxide. This was then treated with carbon monoxide at high temperature and pressure to give technetium carbonyl.

Safe Handling of Technetium

The manipulation of technetium on the sub-gramme scale does not present a health hazard provided some elementary precautions are taken. ^{99}Tc is a weak β emitter (β max = 0.3 MeV) and there are no γ rays, but with large amounts of the element secondary x-rays (Bremstrahlung) may become important. The author always handles technetium in a well ventilated fume cupboard. Normal radiochemical practice is observed, nothing unnecessary is placed into the cupboard and everything removed from the cupboard is monitored. All evaporations are carried out using an infra-red lamp. The vessel containing the technetium is covered by a watch glass and an inverted beaker to reduce contamination by spraying. Care is taken to avoid evaporating solutions of pertechnic acid to prevent losses due to the volatility of technetium heptaoxide. Solids are never transferred dry, they are either dissolved or suspended in a liquid which can later be evaporated off.

References

1. J. C. HINDMAN and P. WEHNER, *J. Am. Chem. Soc.* **75**, 2869 (1953).
2. W. F. JAKOB and B. JEZOWSKA-TRZEBIATOWSKA, *Chem. Ber.* **66B**, 461 (1933).
3. B. JEZOWSKA-TRZEBIATOWSKA, *Roczniki Chem.* **14**, 1061 (1934).
4. E. K. MAUN and N. DAVIDSON, *J. Am. Chem. Soc.* **72**, 2254 (1950).
5. D. F. EVANS, *J. Chem. Soc.* 2003 (1959).
6. H. HOLEMAN, *Z. Anorg. Allgem. Chem.* **220**, 33 (1934).
7. R. H. BUSEY and Q. V. LARSON, *Unclassified Document* O.R.N.L. 2584.
8. P. WEHNER and J. C. HINDMAN, *J. Am. Chem. Soc.* **75**, 2873 (1953).
9. M. S. PLATANOV and S. B. ANISIMOV, *J. Gen. Chem. USSR* 7, 1360 (1937).
10. M. S. PLATANOV, S. B. ANISIMOV and V. M. KRASHENINNIKOVA, *Chem. Ber.* **69B**, 1050 (1936).
11. A. A. BALANDIN, E. I. KARPEISKAYA and A. A. TOLSTOPYATOVA, *Dokl. Akad. Nauk SSSR* **129**, 795 (1959).
12. A. A. BALANDIN, E. I. KARPEISKAYA and A. A. TOLSTOPYATOVA, *Iz. Akad. Nauk SSSR Otd. Khim. Nauk* **1365** (1959).
13. M. S. PLATANOV, S. B. ANISIMOV and V. M. KRASHENINNIKOVA, *Chem. Ber.* **68B**, 761 (1935).

14. H. TROPSCH and R. KASSLER, *Chem. Ber.* **68B**, 2149 (1930).

15. P. F. NI and D. V. SOKOL'SKII, *Izv. Akad. Nauk Kaz. SSR Ser. Khim.* **1**, 46 (1958).

16. J. P. McGEER and H. S. TAYLOR, *J. Am. Chem. Soc.* **73**, 2743 (1951).

17. M. S. PLATANOV and V. I. TOMILOV, *J. Gen. Chem. USSR* **7**, 776 (1937).

18. W. and I. NODDACK, *Brit. Pat.* 346,652 (1929).

19. H. S. BROADBENT, G. C. CAMPBELL, W. J. BARTLEY and J. H. JOHNSON, *J. Org. Chem.* **24**, 1847 (1959).

20. H. S. BROADBENT, L. H. SLAUGH and N. L. JARVIS, *J. Am. Chem. Soc.* **76**, 1519 (1954).

21. H. LINDER and K. DRESCHER, *Chem. Tech. Berlin* **12**, 16 (1960).

22. M. S. PLATANOV, *J. Gen. Chem. USSR* **11**, 683 (1941).

23. H. S. BROADBENT and C. W. WHITTLE, *J. Am. Chem. Soc.* **81**, 3587 (1959).

24. G. H. CARTLEDGE, *J. Phys. Chem.* **59**, 979 (1955).

25. G. H. CARTLEDGE, *J. Phys. Chem.* **60**, 28 (1956).

26. G. H. CARTLEDGE, *J. Phys. Chem.* **60**, 32 (1956).

27. J. C. HILEMAN, D. K. HUGGINS and H. D. KAESZ, *Inorg. Chem.* **1**, 933 (1962).

AUTHOR INDEX

Page numbers in ordinary type are those of citations in the text. Page numbers in *italics* are those where bibliographical references to the stated authors' works are listed at the ends of the chapters

175

SUBJECT INDEX

The letters ff after a page number indicate that the same topic is mentioned again on one or both of the next two following pages.

Amberlite IRA-400 ion exchange resin, 17ff
Ammonium
  perrhenate, 91
  pertechnetate, 42
Anodic oxidation of rhenide ion, 157
Arene complexes, 136
Arsine compounds of rhenium, 107

Barium mesoperrhenate, 40
Beer's Law, 25, 28ff
Bis-π-cyclopentadienyl rhenium hydride, 129
Bis(pyridine) rhenium tricarbonyl iodide, 124
Bis(triphenylphosphine) rhenium carbonyl halides, 125

Caesium tetrachlororhenate, 91
Carbonyl compounds, 115ff
Carbonyl halides, 119ff
Carbonyl halides substitution products, 123ff
Carbonyls reaction with rhenium hexafluoride, 58
Carbonyl—rhenium and technetium carbonyl halides—stretching frequencies, 122
Complex fluorides, 82ff
Complex halides, 82ff
Compounds, cyclopentadienyl, 129, 134
Curie–Weiss law, 68ff, 88
Cyanide and thiocynate complexes, 140
Cyclopentadienyl compounds, 129ff
  rhenium hydrides and deuterides, 129ff, 132

Dowex-50 anion exchange resin, 17ff

Ethylenediamine, 102

Fluororhenates, 83ff

Hexachlororhenate, magnetic properties of, 88
Hexachlorotechnates, 93
Hexafluorotechnates, 87ff

Kotani theory, 84

Molybdenum–rhenium separations, 19ff

Nitrogen ligands, 99ff
Norway, technetium in minerals from, 2

Organorhenium pentacarbonyls, 128ff
Organometallic compounds, 115ff

Perrhenate ion, reduction of electrolytic, 165
  hydrochloric acid, in, 165
  stannous chloride, by, 166
  sulphuric acid, in, 167
Perrhenates, 37ff
  alkali, 37
  properties tabulated, 38ff
Perrhenic acid, 36ff
Perrhenyl chloride, 73
Pertechnetates, crystal structure, 42
Pertechnic acid, 40
Pertechnyl
  chloride, 75ff
  fluoride, 66

183